WATER POLLUTION CONTROL AND ABATEMENT

WATER

Control and

EDITORS:

Ted L. Willrich

ASSOCIATE PROFESSOR
OF AGRICULTURAL ENGINEERING
COLLEGE OF AGRICULTURE
IOWA STATE UNIVERSITY

N. William Hines

ASSOCIATE PROFESSOR OF LAW
COLLEGE OF LAW
UNIVERSITY OF IOWA

**IOWA STATE
UNIVERSITY PRESS**
AMES, IOWA, U.S.A.

POLLUTION
Abatement

The chapters of this book are a result of an
Iowa Water Resources Pollution Control and
Abatement Seminar held at Iowa State University,
Ames, Iowa, November 9–11, 1965.

FOREWORD

In 1955 when the water issue of vital concern to Iowa related to questions of the adequacy and allocation of the state's water supplies, the two state universities responded by convening an assembly of the foremost water specialists within the state to exchange information and ideas on water issues. At this three-day conference, sponsored by the University of Iowa College of Law and the Iowa State University College of Agriculture, were heard the views of experts from all the disciplines, professions, agencies, and specialties having something to contribute to the water allocation discussion. This conference was well received by those who participated and the proceedings were published as a book entitled *Iowa's Water Resources: Sources, Uses, and Laws*. The information collected and views expressed in this volume were heavily relied upon in the drafting of the Water Resources Conservation Act passed by the Iowa Legislature in 1957.

Today the crucial issue is one of water quality. The extent of interest in water quality is amply demonstrated by the fact that in 1965 both the Iowa legislature and the United States Congress enacted significant legislation relating to water pollution control. Prior to the passage of these most recent acts, however, water resource specialists at Iowa State University and the University of Iowa had decided that the time had arrived for a second state water resources conference. In January of 1964 planning for the proposed conference was begun. Again the College of Agriculture and the College of Law assumed the leadership in the enterprise and the cochairmen named for the conference were Dr. T. L. Willrich of Iowa State and Professor N. W. Hines of Iowa. A planning committee was created to assist the cochairmen in organizing the conference. Serving on this committee were Dr. E. R. Baumann and Dr. J. F. Timmons of Iowa State University, and Dr. H. S. Smith and Dr. Marshall Harris of the University of Iowa. Much of the credit for the success of the conference must go to this planning committee which guided the project through its formative stages.

The development of the program and the recruitment of outstanding participants are both clearly evidenced by the published proceedings reported hereinafter. The conference was held November 9–11, 1965, in Ames, Iowa, and was well attended by water resource persons. If a conference of this type may be measured by the quality of the intellectual exchange that occurs, all in attendance would doubtless agree that it was a highly successful event.

The College of Law and the College of Agriculture were pleased to be able to sponsor this 1965 Water Resources Conference and also to assist in the publication of this book. It is hoped that this publication will assist the people of Iowa in evaluating the complex issues associated with the water pollution problem, and that through conferences like this progress can be made toward assuring a future of cleanliness for Iowa's water resources.

FLOYD ANDRE, *Dean*
College of Agriculture,
Iowa State University,
Ames, Iowa

MASON LADD, *Dean*
College of Law,
University of Iowa,
Iowa City, Iowa

PREFACE

No more important single problem faces this country today than the problem of "good water." Water is our greatest single natural resource. The issue of pure water must be settled now for the benefit not only of this generation but for untold generations to come. The need for good quality water for all of our Nation's uses—public and private—is a paramount one.

So spoke the House Committee on Public Works in reporting on the federal Water Quality Act of 1965. The deep concern manifested by this pronouncement accurately reflects the current high level of public awareness and anxiety relating to the deplorable state of many of our waters. No longer is water pollution control a subject of interest only to public health officers and a few wildlife conservation enthusiasts; it has ascended to a position among the most prominent of current domestic issues.

Although recognition of water pollution as a problem of national concern is important to generation of the support essential to its solution, water pollution control is still primarily a local matter. If meaningful headway is to be made against water pollution, it must be accomplished at the state level. State and local regulatory agencies must police the quality of our waters, investigate complaints, create and apply the water quality standards, and, when necessary, enforce the penalties against violators.

Effective pollution control requires the coexistence of at least three factors: (1) a sincere state commitment to clean waters manifested in a workable regulatory scheme, (2) high levels of knowledge and dedication on

the part of the state officials charged with administration
of the control program, and (3) public understanding of
the nature of the pollution problem and support for the
control efforts.

In 1965 Iowa took a great stride in the direction of
effective pollution control with the passage, by the Sixty-
first General Assembly, of the Water Pollution Control
Law and the subsequent creation of a new control commission. This new water pollution control scheme holds
great promise for cleaning up Iowa's waters. The regulatory scheme is modern, the personnel charged with administration of the program are energetic public servants
of the highest caliber, and the whole attitude of the state
government toward pollution control appears more vigor-
ous.

However, several of the important factors mentioned
above cannot be built into a control program. The decisions of a control commission can be no sounder than the
basic information and insights concerning water pollution
upon which they act. Assuring that the decision makers
have ready access to current knowledge in the many
areas involved in pollution control decisions is a matter
of extreme importance. Contained in the following pages
are papers and comments prepared by some of the most
learned men in their fields in the country. Here there
will be found an unusually complete collection of the
knowledge and views of scholars and practitioners in
the fields most directly involved in water pollution control. In marshalling and making available the learning of
specialists in these many areas, a conference such as the
one reported in this book may make an invaluable contribution to the cause of water pollution control.

Another essential to an effective water pollution control program is an informed and sympathetic public.
Even if the control commission is deliberately engaged
in extensive public relations work, it is doubtful that it
could achieve the same impact on the public mind and
conscience as is worked by the cumulative effect of the
papers published in this book. This conference and the
publication of its proceedings should serve to stir the
interest of Iowans in the protection of their precious
water resources and thereby help mobilize public opinion
to support the activities of the new control commission.

The three parts of this book are designed to overlap

somewhat. It was hoped that this approach would insure reasonably full coverage of this multifaceted problem. Part I presents the pollution problem as seen through the specialized vision of four different disciplines: engineering, economics, law, and political science. Part II is concerned with the Iowa situation. Part III shifts the analysis from the various disciplines to the interest groups most often involved in conflicts over pollution issues: municipalities, industry, agriculture, and outdoor recreation.

The materials contained in this volume should be both informative and useful. However, this book is a mere scratch on the surface of the body of knowledge that will be required to cope adequately with the present and emerging problems of water pollution control. It is hoped the information and ideas contained herein will stimulate others to undertake research in this most vital and challenging field—water resources management.

TED L. WILLRICH   N. WILLIAM HINES
Iowa State University   University of Iowa

ACKNOWLEDGMENT

THE SEMINAR REPORTED ON HEREIN WAS COSPONSORED BY the Iowa State Water Resources Research Institute, the Water Resources Council of the University of Iowa, the Graduate College and the Water Resources Advisory Committee of Iowa State University, in addition to the College of Law of the University of Iowa and the College of Agriculture of Iowa State University.

Subvention for publication of this book was paid from funds provided by the United States Department of the Interior as authorized under the Water Resources Research Act of 1964, Public Law 88-379.

Editorial assistance was furnished in part through a grant from IOWA COMMUNITY SERVICES under Title I of the Higher Education Act of 1965.

CONTENTS

S.C.S. PHOTO

PART 1:

Small reservoirs provide
excellent swimming,
fishing, and water
supplies. Large reservoirs,
with corresponding
larger watersheds,
require more control
to minimize water quality
degradation and
siltation.

VIEWPOINTS OF VARIOUS DISCIPLINES

CHAPTER 1

SCOPE AND CHALLENGE OF THE WATER POLLUTION SITUATION

ALLEN V. KNEESE

INTEREST IN THE PROBLEM OF WATER QUALITY IS INTENSE AND NUMEROUS congressional hearings on the matter have been held. The Senate Select Committee on Water Resources in the early 1960's completed a far-reaching study with heavy emphasis on water quality, and the daily press carries articles on one or another aspect of water pollution with great frequency. Almost all the major national news and business magazines from time to time carry feature articles stressing water quality problems. Sometimes these accounts, in their search for spectacular material, have emphasized gross, but comparatively easy to solve, problems instead of building an understanding of the more subtle but also more challenging ones. Nevertheless, they are the strongest possible evidence of immense public concern with water quality.

NATIONAL AND INTERSTATE POLLUTION CONTROL

On the legal side, a number of national laws dealing with federal participation in pollution control activities have been passed. Starting with the federal Water Pollution Control Act of 1948, the role of the federal government has been steadily increased. We have seen in 1965 a new federal law which greatly expands federal authority in the field. In addition to setting stream quality standards, if the states do not set their own within a two-year time limit, the complex of federal legisla-

ALLEN V. KNEESE is director, Water Resources Program, Resources for the Future, Inc. The views expressed are those of the author and not necessarily of his organization. Some of the material used in this chapter is from the author's *The Economics of Regional Water Quality Management*, The Johns Hopkins University Press, 1963.

tion now provides for the inclusion of water quality control storage in federal reservoirs, making of comprehensive water quality control plans, subsidies to municipalities for construction of water treatment plants, and extensive enforcement powers against individual polluters. State and interstate activities have also been notable; for example, the signing of the Delaware River Basin Commission Compact may become a United States landmark in effective management of water quality.

There is no doubt that the pollution control efforts which have now been under way for some years have already borne some fruit. Despite the pronouncements of the more lurid popular articles during the late 1950's and early 1960's the condition of the mainstems of some of our most heavily used streams has improved markedly. In the eastern United States this achievement has been somewhat obscured by the extraordinarily low flow of rivers during the latter part of that time. Nevertheless, in the Delaware, the Ohio, and the Potomac, for example, many of the highly offensive materials that once floated down these rivers are now removed from the effluents before they enter the stream. This is, no doubt, in considerable measure due to effective but limited interstate pollution control bodies on these streams. For instance, the Interstate Commission on the Delaware, which was the predecessor of the Delaware River Basin Compact, wrote an impressive record for getting basic treatment facilities built by most municipalities and many industries. The record of ORSANCO, the Ohio River Valley Sanitation Commission, is even more impressive. When ORSANCO was formed in 1948, less than 1 per cent of the sewered population in the basin had any form of treatment. At the present time over 90 per cent are treating their wastes, mostly by mechanical means which remove at least the grosser materials in them. It should also be realized that virtually all of this was accomplished before federal subsidies were available to the municipalities. Many individual states and municipalities elsewhere also made great progress especially in the matter of keeping the raw sewage solids, oil, blood, hair, animal carcasses, and other highly offensive solids, so beloved of newspaper story writers, out of their streams.

Nevertheless, serious problems of water quality still confront the nation. Their solution will lie not only in the fields of biological, physical, and engineering sciences but will require the very best efforts of economists, lawyers, and public administrators as well.

ECONOMIC CONSIDERATION

There is ample evidence that the costs imposed on water users through the remaining residual discharge of wastes into watercourses are large, and potential costs are increasing rapidly. In response to this situation cities and industries have been required, or may be required, to undertake enormous investments in comparatively sophisticated waste disposal facilities and technology. Moreover, with rapidly rising discretionary income the value placed on the very high quality water needed for many recreational purposes will rise strongly and, indeed, this demand more than any other accounts for the present level of interest in water pollution control.

Economists and others have long known that the economic institutions on which we customarily rely to balance costs and returns for the use of resources—the interaction of market forces in a private enterprise system—do not perform this function satisfactorily for waste disposal. In deciding how to dispose of its wastes, an upstream firm or city is not induced by the market to take into account the costs imposed on downstream water users or the value of water use opportunities foreclosed by its effluent discharge. Furthermore, there are often economies of scale in waste disposal which cannot be realized by an individual firm or city acting independently.

As a result of these factors market forces are supplemented in a variety of ways. Civic responsibility is invoked to reduce waste contribution to watercourses. Damaged parties may resort to adversary proceedings in courts of law. Financial inducement to encourage waste treatment by municipalities are offered by the federal government, and storage to augment low flows is provided at federal expense. No doubt these practices have contributed a great deal toward reducing the side effects associated with waste disposal.

These unintended but unavoidable effects on other potential or actual users of watercourses are called "external" or "off-site" effects by the economist. This obtuse terminology is really quite understandable upon a moment's reflection. External costs are those borne by a decision-making unit other than that which causes them. The word "costs" is used in a broad sense. It encompasses the reduced fishing opportunity downstream from a factory as well as the increased water treatment cost imposed on another industrial user.

But so far in the application of conventional control practices, there has not been a systematic balancing of costs and returns to achieve maximum benefits from an optimum system for the control of waste disposal. Since any water pollution control procedure involves costs as well as benefits, an optimum or balanced situation does not involve stopping waste discharge completely but rather controlling it at the best level. In other words, the problem becomes one of management—not complete prohibition.

WATER QUALITY MANAGEMENT

The concept of water quality management raises three main issues.

1. How do we determine the quality of water it is desirable to maintain in our streams? This is the question which Congress threw right in the lap of the states in 1965 by giving them two years to establish water quality standards for their interstate rivers.
2. How do we devise the best physical system for achieving that quality? Clearly, this is a question of economics and administration as well as engineering.
3. How do we determine the best organizational and institutional arrangements for administering and managing water quality.

Determination of Water Quality

Before long most of our streams will be free of the grossest and most obvious forms of pollution such as floating and suspended matter. This result follows from the fact that it is now widely accepted that the social costs, or external costs, of permitting such pollution outweigh the cost of eliminating it, at least in populated areas. Also, this type of pollution can be controlled in a comparatively efficient way by treatment at individual outfalls. Unfortunately, this minimal type of treatment is not sufficient for optimum water quality management in many instances where demands on the stream are heavy or the summer season flows are low. Residual discharges may still deplete dissolved oxygen and kill fish or produce various kinds of difficulties in the preparation of water for municipal and industrial uses. Moreover, the concept of primary or mechanical treatment is often of only limited applicability or significance in the case of industrial waste streams which contain more finely divided or dissolved materials.

Accordingly, once primary or mechanical treatment is provided, we still face the question of what qualities of water are appropriate for the many uses of watercourses. It is one thing to remove fecal solids from the stream and another to assure that residual organic wastes do not interfere with fish culture by causing periodic deterioration of oxygen supplies. It is one thing to remove oil from an industrial effluent and another to assure that residual phenols do not impose an increased treatment cost upon downstream municipal water users. We are encountering also a whole new array of pollutants which may have little effect on the appearance of water but whose other effects can be costly and widespread. These pollutants can impose treatment costs on successive users, damage facilities of various kinds, make it necessary to turn to alternative sources of water, and reduce the value of water for recreation.

Decisions must be made, for the conflicts among water uses are becoming stronger as economic development increases the demand on watercourses. Means must be found to balance the valuable use of watercourses for waste disposal against other valuable, and usually conflicting, uses such as municipal and industrial water supply and recreation. To argue that all wastes should be kept out of streams may be idealistic, but it is also unrealistic and inconsistent with the value that people put on inexpensive manufactured products and uses of their income other than for environmental sanitation. A very rough calculation indicates that it might cost between $15 and $20 billion a year, under current conditions of economic development, to give literal meaning to the often repeated but seldom analyzed idea that streams should be kept as clean as possible by removing all residual wastes from effluents. It is clear that there is no escape from making some type of an analysis of the costs and returns of pollution control. The valuation problem cannot be avoided. Either we face it squarely or hide it under sanctimonious statements concerning standards and "professional judgment." Unfortunately, research on these matters by economists has been minimal. If water quality standards are to be in any way related to an economic optimum which balances costs and returns, we must learn much more about the benefits associated with water quality improvement and do so quickly.

Systems for Determining Water Quality

A second major issue which water quality management raises concerns the engineering-economic systems available for achieving a desirable level of water quality. Particularly, when gross floating and suspended materials have been removed from effluents, quality control moves beyond treatment in individual municipal and industrial treatment plants and can be managed in a number of ways. Because the level of stream flow effects water quality, it may be feasible to store water in large reservoirs during periods of high flow and release it during low flows or to store wastes temporarily and release them when flows are high. Measures such as artificial reaeration of the rivers themselves can also be undertaken to enhance the self-purification capacity. Furthermore, in the matter of industrial wastes, reclamation and process changes can reduce waste loads. Industrial waste loads are exceedingly important; indeed, it has been estimated that industry contributes twice as much biochemical oxygen demand to the nation's streams as all municipalities combined and generates and discharges even more of most other polluting materials. In broad perspective even the location of economic activities becomes an important determinant of the cost of waste disposal and water supply facilities.

Our present policies and institutional arrangements seem quite deficient for realizing the economies which may be obtained from the planning and orderly implementation of regional waste disposal systems in our more heavily developed areas. Current policies of direct regulation of waste discharges combined with nonreimbursable low-flow augmentation are likely to fall pretty far short of reaching optimum systems for waste control. To use direct regulation in the form of an effluent standard implies a vast knowledge of the opportunities which are available for industrial process redesign and the treatment of rather esoteric wastes. Moreover, it does nothing to realize the economies which can be achieved through regional measures which capitalize upon geographical and hydrological factors to reduce the costs associated with waste disposal.

USE OF EFFLUENT CHARGE

An effluent charge or tax, which is weighted by the relative damaging effect of various effluents and which could be used to finance measures on a regional scale, has much to commend it in this connection. The charge would exert continuing pressure on industry to utilize currently available technologies to an optimal extent. It would tend to concentrate waste reduction at those points where it can be most economically achieved and would provide an incentive to develop the technology of waste reduction. A properly structured effluent charge would always permit industry to earn a benefit in the terms of a reduced charge when it cuts down on the waste load even to the lowest possible level of water discharge. The proceeds from such a charge could be used to develop measures such as flow regulation, efficient large-scale regional treatment systems which collect and treat wastes from a number of industries and municipalities, mechanical reaeration of streams to enhance their self-purification capacity, etc., to the extent that the benefits of implementing such activities exceed the costs.

This combination of approaches—an effluent charge and systematic identification, evaluation, and implementation of a wide range of measures of a regional or river basin type—has been used with great success in the Ruhr area of West Germany. The streams which serve the Ruhr region have a very low flow during the summer season—about 400 cubic feet per second or only about half the lowest flow ever recorded on the Potomac River. The population of the area is around 10 million and it is perhaps the world's most heavily industrialized region. Forty per cent of the industrial production of Germany occurs here, including over 80 per cent of the heavy industrial output. All this is in an area approximately 50 miles wide and 100 miles long. The waste disposal demands within this region are immense, yet major sections of the river are so managed that the stream is suitable for recreational purposes including swimming and boating. Moreover, prices of unsubsidized, publicly supplied water are as low as or lower than any of the major urban areas of Germany. These results have been attained by cooperative regional management authorities known as *Genossenschaften*.

The following features are central to the success of the system developed by these organizations:

1. The engineering system has been specifically designed to meet the needs of the Ruhr region. It is a unique system within Germany.

2. Waste disposal is managed on a regionwide basis in which advantage is taken of economies resulting from flow regulation and large-scale treatment and recovery of potential waste products. The regenerative capacity of the streams is utilized to the extent consistent with water quality standards which are based on a variety of water uses in the area.

3. One stream in the region is used in a completely specialized way, being dedicated to waste disposal use only.

4. Industries and cities pay a charge for the effluent they contribute to the waste disposal system based upon periodic tests of the quality and quantity of their effluent. The charge which is levied is not contingent upon whether the wastes are directly handled in treatment plants or not. In other words, an efficient regional system of works is designed and then charges are distributed in accordance with at least a rough measure of the cost of receiving the specific effluents into the system as a whole. Moreover, municipalities and industrial plants can always reduce their charges by reducing the amount of waste discharged into the system.

Impressive results have followed from this system. The effluent charge has proved an effective means of motivating industries to reduce contribution of waste to rivers—sometimes to an extreme extent. Using the geographic and hydrologic features of the particular river basin in an imaginative and systematic manner to minimize waste disposal costs has undoubtedly reduced costs for the region as a whole. A good illustration of this is the fact that municipalities and industries always have the option of building their own waste treatment plants and thereby reducing the effluent charges levied upon them. Up to this point not a single municipality or industry has chosen to follow this route.

The density of the development in this area has perhaps meant that particularly large gains could be achieved by systematic regional approaches. Nevertheless, it seems that resting our program of pollution control on the two pillars of conventional treatment and nonreimbursable flow augmentation has caused us to overlook opportunities to achieve major economies through a more flexible approach, even in less highly developed areas of the United States. For example, Robert Davis of RFF has completed a case study of the Potomac Basin in which he considered a number of alternatives including mechanical reaeration, diversion of wastes from critical areas, and periodic programmed introduction of advanced waste treatment at particular treatment plants. He was able to find many combinations of systems less costly than the combination of flow augmentation and conventional waste treatment which had been previously proposed for the basin by the federal planning agencies.

Also, the presently unorthodox possibility of using effluent charges in the United States context has attracted considerable interest. Statements more or less sympathetic to this approach have appeared in a variety of widely distributed magazines and newspapers including *Fortune, Time,* and *The Wall Street Journal*. At the national level a committee, headed by Gardner Ackley, Chief of the President's Council of Economic Advisors, and consisting of representatives of various interested agencies, has been working for over a year on a report assessing the merits of effluent charges. The report had not been released by November, 1965, (perhaps it never will be) but it is understood that the effluent charge concept received careful attention. A report of the President's Science Advisory Committee also stresses the concept. The adoption of effluent charges as a national policy could be a major step toward effective and efficient water quality management.

Actually, the matter of regional systems and effluent charges is closely interrelated with the third issue, suggested earlier, which water quality management raises; that is, how to determine the best institutional arrangements for administering and managing water quality. The combination of policies at the federal, interstate, state, and local government levels have been very important in encouraging an important reduction of the most offensive elementary forms of pollution.

ROLE OF REGIONAL ORGANIZATION

There is, however, much doubt as to how much further present policies can go toward confronting the challenge of efficient and effective water quality management. This will take imaginative and continuing activity on a detailed regional or river basin level. Yet, there is a notable absence of regional agencies or authorities which can flexibly plan, finance, and construct the most efficient river basin systems for waste disposal. The Delaware River Basin Commission is the only potential exception, and it remains to be tested. The policy of the federal government should be redirected toward encouraging experimentation with new techniques of control and new institutional devices. Accordingly, in testimony before the Subcommittee on Air and Water Pollution of the Senate Committee on Public Works I have described a possible new and hopefully constructive form of federal initiative. I have suggested that the federal government consider incentives for the organization and operation of regional agencies with genuine authority to implement programs of waste management either under state law or through interstate compacts and that the federal government use its authority to establish the principle of effluent charges.

Incentives for regional organizations might be provided in the following manner. Upon creation of an agency with adequate authority to institute an efficient regional system, the agency would be eligible for a grant of funds to support a share of its operating costs while it assembled and analyzed pertinent data and designed its program. If the federal government is satisfied that the program would meet reasonable objectives, the agency might be eligible for a grant to assist it with its operating expenses for a limited time. The regional agency might also be made eligible for federal loans for investment in large-scale facilities where scale economies can be achieved.

Finally, and perhaps most important, the federal government could establish minimum effluent standards (basically a requirement for primary or mechanical treatment to remove the grossly offensive materials mentioned earlier) and a policy of levying charges upon effluents. These policies would help to eliminate the relative disadvantage in competing for new industry under which particular regional agencies would otherwise labor if an effluent charge were levied. This program would also provide acceptable performance, even in instances where regional authorities do not become established, while opening the door for creation of such agencies and flexible planning and implementation of programs on their part. Once such a regional agency was duly established, the authority and responsibility for levying effluent charges would be turned over to it. The agency should refine the system of effluent charges as a tool of management, since in areas without regional agencies having continuing responsibility for water quality the charge might—for administrative reasons—need to be based upon rather crude rules of thumb and self-monitoring by waste dischargers. In both cases, however, it would be very important that the charges be levied in such a way that the waste discharger could reduce or avoid them by reducing his waste quantity. Otherwise, the incentive effect would be lost. For the established regional agency the charge would provide a source of revenue to be used to design, implement, and operate a system making flexible use of the full array of efficient means for dealing with the problem.

It has not been practical here to deal in a systematic manner with possible alternatives to this particular proposal. Such alternatives will undoubtedly be discussed and perhaps implemented. Our new challenges in environmental quality, of which water pollution is a major one, will require that we break out of old and comfortable modes of thought and devise means of making a constructive response to new situations, not only in the scientific and engineering fields but in the areas of economics, law, administration, and institutions as well.

CHAPTER 2

PHYSICAL, SCIENTIFIC, AND ENGINEERING ASPECTS OF POLLUTION

E. ROBERT BAUMANN

(2)

WHEREVER WE FIND~~~MAN,~~ WE NECESSARILY MUST FIND THE WASTES PRO-
duced by man's activities. Such wastes inevitably will find their way
into the air, the soil, or the waters near the point at which the wastes
are produced. Since matter cannot be created or destroyed, man's activities serve merely to change the form of matter and the place and
concentration in which it is to be found in nature. Air, soil, or water
pollution occurs only when the change in the form of matter and its
location and concentration in nature's scheme of things is such as to
create a nuisance, to impair its subsequent usefulness, or to interfere
with nature's balance.

Since pollution and its control is a complex and difficult problem,
it is essential to approach the topic of water pollution with a clear
understanding of the physical, scientific, and engineering aspects involved in its prevention, control, and abatement. In order to start from
a common base, let us consider five simple questions:

1. What is pollution?
2. Where does it come from?
3. How do we measure pollution?
4. Why should we be concerned about pollution?
5. What are we doing about it?

E. ROBERT BAUMANN is professor of civil engineering, Iowa State
University, Ames, Iowa.

13

WHAT IS POLLUTION?

The gaseous, liquid, and solid constituents of water which affect water quality may be grouped into four general classifications depending on whether their presence in water would (1) not be permissible, (2) be undesirable or objectionable, (3) be permissible but not necessarily desirable, and (4) be desirable. The placing of a particular constituent of water into one of these classifications will depend on the ultimate use of the water. For example, if the water to which the constituent is added were to be used immediately for animal consumption, the presence of toxic compounds would not be desirable; however, the presence of a certain amount of oxygen would not be objectionable. If, on the other hand, the water were to be used in a power plant for steam generation, the presence of toxic materials might be permissible or even desirable while the oxygen would be objectionable since it would lead to unnecessary equipment corrosion.

In view of the large number of different uses of water, a number of different standards of stream quality have been developed. Usages which are available as measures of permissible pollution include: (1) preservation of natural-state (so-called wild) river, (2) use as a source of potable water supply, (3) preservation of fish and wildlife, (4) safety for agricultural use such as stock watering and irrigation, (5) safety for recreational use such as swimming and water skiing, (6) use for industrial purposes such as cooling and process water, (7) freedom from nuisance, (8) commercial use such as navigation, and (9) use for water-carriage of wastes. In each case the standards for water quality adopted must be developed on the basis of public health, esthetic, and economic considerations.

Obviously, it is not practical or realistic to define rigidly what we mean by pollution since the determination of whether a certain constituent creates a nuisance, impairs the usefulness of the water, or interferes with nature's balance must depend on the subsequent use which is to be made of the water. The assignment of a particular standard of subsequent use to a particular stream is difficult. The public health, esthetic, and economic considerations are so broad in concept that an interdisciplinary approach must be used in establishing a reasonable balance between competing uses if public interests are to be served.

Many states have water pollution control agencies that are composed of representatives of different interest groups and disciplines involved in water resources activities. These agencies operate at a state or drainage basin level to take into consideration the ultimate economic use of the water and to establish the stream standard to protect that use. Thus, they serve to outline in detail exactly what constitutes pollution in each case. In establishing a standard of quality for a receiving body of water, the water pollution control agency must consider the current and future water needs of the entire region. No community or industry which produces a liquid waste can be considered as an isolated unit but must be considered as an integral part of the drainage basin in which it is located. The waters in the basin may be used for a source of water supply, for recreation, and for receiving wastes. All these uses represent benefits obtained by the public. However, the use of the water for receiving wastes is not always compatible with its use for water supply and for recreation. The standard of permissible pollution, therefore, must be established on a basis that will bring to the public which inhabits the basin the greatest benefit for the least cost.

In order to do this, the available water resource of the basin must be evaluated adequately and the need for the water projected into the future. This implies that we have the ability to evaluate the economic feasibility of alternate means of meeting future demands for water supply, recreation water, and water pollution control. The added cost of waste treatment for water pollution control must be measured against the value of fish or recreation to be preserved. It would not be economically wise to spend $50,000 per year to operate a water pollution control plant to protect $1,000 worth of fish. On the other hand it would not be economically sound to destroy even $10 of a water resource's value "to save" $10 worth of waste treatment cost. In general the standard for permissible pollution should be such as to provide a ratio of benefits to cost of at least 1:1.

Once the stream use has been determined, some criteria must be established on which the engineer can base the treatment which a waste must be given before it is discharged to a stream. These criteria may be established by the creation of *stream standards* or *waste effluent standards*. If the water pollution agency establishes stream standards, the engineer is charged with the responsibility of determining what degree of treatment must be given a particular waste so that the stream standard is always maintained. The volume and complexity of wastes will increase with time and population growth. The degree of treatment afforded each waste will also have to increase just to maintain the stream standard. In effect the establishment of stream standards puts the burden of predicting the future on the shoulders of each design engineer. The establishment of *effluent standards*, on the other hand, gives the design engineer a clear and precise standard which a waste effluent must meet. Thus, the burden of predicting the future is placed where it belongs—in the hands of the water pollution control agency.

WHERE DOES POLLUTION COME FROM?

Pollution of streams results from man's activities in the home, in the factory, and on the farm. In the home water is used for many purposes, most of which involve adding to the solids content of the water. For example, water is used for washing people, clothing, food, and cars, and for carrying away ground garbage, human wastes, and even waste foods. Milk fed to children is an excellent food, but milk poured down the drain is a significant source of pollution.

The "ABS" or detergent problem resulting from domestic water use created many difficulties. The ABS detergent was produced by the chemical industry as an ideal washing compound. Unfortunately, it was biologically nondegradable and relatively unaffected by conventional waste treatment methods. In wastes it produced foam in rivers and interfered with normal water and waste treatment. Unable to adapt existing treatments to handle it, we ultimately resorted to discarding the ABS detergent and depended on the chemical industry to develop—which they did—a new detergent which could be handled in conventional treatment systems.

In Iowa significant pollution also results from agriculturally based industry. Our meat packing industry, our dairy industry, and our canning industry all use large amounts of water for processing food products. The used water contains large quantities of blood, dirt, offal from the animals, waste milk, and vegetable processing wastes. In total the polluting power of such industrial wastes will exceed the polluting power of the wastes from a strictly domestic population. In many Iowa cities the waste from industries will produce a pollution problem ten, even twenty, times that resulting from the cities' human population.

It is relatively easy to isolate and identify stream pollution resulting from human or industrial pollution since such wastes enter a stream in relatively fixed sewer outlets. It is not so easy to isolate and identify pollution resulting from farming activities since the pollution may enter streams only during and immediately following storms producing surface runoff or deep infiltration. However, in Iowa the stream pollution potential from farm operations far exceeds the pollution potential of Iowa's cities and industries. For example, Iowa produces approximately 22 million hogs for market each year. At any one time about 9 million hogs are on feed and are producing animal wastes. Each hog produces, according to recent studies conducted at Iowa State University, a waste strength equivalent to the waste of four people. Thus, our hogs alone produce waste equivalent to a human population of 36 million people. This is nine times as great as the waste from our cities.

Until recently this swine waste was spread rather uniformly across all the farms of Iowa, as were the cattle, chicken, and turkey wastes.

However, with the increased mechanization of farming and the definite trend to confinement production of swine, cattle, and turkeys, more and more of these wastes are concentrated in populated areas in large feeding operations. For example, the ISU swine confinement feeding operation puts 800 hogs and wastes equivalent to 3,200 people on a single concrete floor. Other similar operations housing up to 25,000 swine have been in operation in Iowa. Wastes from such confinement feeding present difficult treatment problems if they are to be handled economically and effectively.

In many such feeding operations the feed rations include minute quantities of specific products to increase pork production. For example, swine feed rations incorporate small quantities of copper oxide and antibiotics to cut down intestinal disorders. These same products have a similar antibiotic effect in the wastes and interfere with normal waste treatment methods.

The increased capacity for corn production, which has resulted in an increase from 60 to 85 bushels per acre in 10–12 years, has been realized at the expense of stream pollution. To increase corn yields, farmers have learned to use fertilizers, insecticides, herbicides, and weed killers effectively. To meet the demand, Iowa industries have tooled up to produce these effective chemicals; but when washed into streams, as they are sure to be, they will also be effective in killing fish and other aquatic life and in providing nutrients for plant growth in the streams. For example, toxaphene in water in concentrations as small as 3.5 parts per billion can kill fish.

The big growth in corn production has been due primarily to increased use of fertilizer. The nitrates and phosphates deliberately applied to crops to increase plant growth are also the chemicals which encourage plant growth—algae—in streams. It is easy to say we must cease stream pollution by prohibiting the discharge of such pollutants to streams. It is much more difficult to do, for it might mean the curtailment of modern discoveries which contribute so much to agricultural production.

Man's activities are the producers of wastes. However, the time is long since past when human fecal matter constitutes the bulk of the pollution-causing wastes. Technology is ever advancing and new products are developed and old ones abandoned before the pollution significance of some of them can even be determined. Today 75 per cent of drugstore prescriptions involve drugs unknown five years ago. In many chemical industries the majority of sales involves products unknown two or three years previously. Thus, the source of wastes and their complexity can be expected to increase directly with the growth of industry, particularly the chemical industry.

HOW DO WE MEASURE POLLUTION?

To be able to abate or eliminate pollution, it is first necessary to be able to measure the amount of pollution involved. Usually this is done by measuring both the volume and the strength of a waste. The volume of a waste is measured in terms of the total flow in gallons per day or in a per capita flow expressed in gallons per capita per day. In Iowa the normal per capita flow of domestic sewage will vary from about 50 (small towns) to about 150 (large cities) gallons per capita per day.

The strength of a waste is expressed both by the type and amount of solids it contains and by the biological activity which these solids will support. Simply stated, most wastes involved in stream pollution consist primarily of solids suspended and dissolved in water. These solids will consist of both organic and inorganic materials. The organic materials—those representing living or dead plant and animal matter—serve as food for microorganisms and constitute the major pollution-producing solids. Such organic solids are composed of carbon, oxygen, hydrogen, nitrogen, and sulfur (COHNS) and can be burned readily. Examples of organic materials include fecal material, paper, bacteria, ABS detergents, and a host of others.

Inorganic solids include those fixed minerals which remain if the organic solids are burned off. They include such solids as sand, ash, and similar materials. In normal domestic wastes approximately 60 per cent of the solids will be organic and 40 per cent will be inorganic.

The weight of solids in a waste is expressed in units of concentration, ppm (pounds of solid per million pounds of waste) or in terms of total weight (pounds per day). One of the major problems in measuring pollutional constituents in a waste is the fact that they are present in such small concentrations. Solids may be present in concentrations of a hundred to several thousand parts per million (ppm). Oxygen is normally present in concentrations up to about 10 parts per million. Some exotic chemicals of pollutional significance may present problems in concentrations of less than 1 part per billion (ppb).

The following formulas show the typical composition of a domestic sewage.

Ton of typical domestic sewage: 1999 pounds water (99.95% water)
$$\underline{\qquad\qquad\qquad 1 \text{ pound solids } (0.05\% \text{ solids})}$$
$$2000 \text{ pounds waste}$$

Solids per capita = about 0.50 pound
Waste volume per capita = 80–120 gallons
$$\text{Solids concentration} = \frac{0.50 \times 10^6}{80 \times 8.33} = 750 \text{ ppm}$$
or

$$\frac{0.50 \times 10^6}{120 \times 8.33} = 500 \text{ ppm}$$

Total Solids = Dissolved solids + Suspended solids
1 pound = 0.5 pound   + 0.5 pound
500 ppm = 250 ppm   + 250 ppm
Total Solids = Organic solids   + Inorganic solids
1 pound = 0.6 pound   + 0.4 pound
500 ppm = 300 ppm   + 200 ppm

If each person daily contributes about 0.5 pound of solids per 120 gallons of waste, the solids concentration will approximate 500 ppm in addition to the solids normally present in tap water. A solids concentration of 500 ppm represents the presence of only 1 pound of solids in each ton of waste. Of the one pound of solids, about 0.5 pound will be in solution (like sugar and salt) and 0.5 pound will be in suspension (like paper and coffee grounds). Of the 0.5 pound of solids in suspension, about 0.25 pound will settle out on quiescent standing (the coffee grounds and paper) and about 0.25 pound will remain in suspension (the colloidal solids). If we go back to the original 1 pound of solids, 0.6 pound will consist of organic solids and 0.4 pound will be inorganic solids.

The solids tests give us a measure of the total amount of solids in a waste and their relative division into suspended and dissolved fractions and into organic and inorganic fractions. Solids tests, however, do not indicate any specific information concerning the susceptibility of this waste to treatment or the pollutional effect of the waste. Such information is provided by additional chemical (chemical oxygen demand or COD) and biological (biochemical oxygen demand or BOD) tests which are made more routinely to determine the amount of oxygen required to stabilize the waste. The COD test measures the oxygen requirement chemically by determining the amount of a chemical oxidizing agent, such as potassium dichromate, required to completely oxidize the organic material present in a sample. The BOD test measures the amount of oxygen required for the biological decomposition of organic solids to occur under aerobic conditions at a standardized time (normally five days) and temperature (normally 20°C). The BOD is the major test made to determine the polluting power of a waste, because it measures the total amount and rate of oxygen which will be needed to prevent odor nuisance and oxygen depletion of streams. Thus, it is the single most important test on which the engineer bases the design of waste treatment facilities.

It does not, however, provide any information concerning the many new and unusual wastes now encountered which contribute to the water pollution problem—ABS, herbicides, insecticides, weed killers, acid wastes, residual dissolved organics, plating wastes, and many others. If such wastes are suspected as a source of pollution—or are manufactured or used in a stream basin—specialized tests have to be developed and made to determine their presence. For some of these, standard tests are available. For others, tests are nonexistent or inaccurate. For many (toxaphene, for example) it may be easier to develop a bioassay test (using fish to determine the pollutant concentration by measuring its effect in killing specific fish) than to develop specific quantitative chemical tests accurate for use with dilute solutions where pollution concentrations are measured in parts per billion.

In some cases the tests require so much expensive equipment in addition to a skilled chemist that only one or two laboratories in a state are able to run a given test. To be able to measure pesticides in dilute solution in water supplies, a laboratory will require use of chromatographic equipment costing $10,000–$15,000. In addition the technician must acquire specialized experience if he is to operate the equipment and evaluate the findings accurately. At present only the State Hygienic Laboratories in Iowa City are equipped adequately to determine pesticides in water on a routine basis. Although they will analyze single samples for pesticides, compensation requested for the analysis of large numbers of samples in a proposed research study at Iowa State was estimated at a cost of $100 per sample. Such costs mean that few pesticide pollution studies can be conducted in Iowa until pollution has already occurred and the political situation demands a solution.

The major needs in the area of pollution measurement include the following:

1. The need to develop quantitative techniques for the measurement of specific pollutants now of concern and for all potential pollutants which may be of concern in the future.
2. The need to develop a "pool" of chemists and technicians qualified to analyze waste samples for specific pollutants.
3. The need to develop a laboratory or laboratories adequately equipped and willing to provide "service analysis" of specific pollutants on a reasonable cost basis. Such analyses will be of help to Iowa industries in preventing pollution and to university research personnel working in pollution-related areas who do not have the personnel or funds required to maintain a continued competence in analysis for all of the specific pollutants.

WHY BE CONCERNED ABOUT POLLUTION?

For years health educators have preached against water pollution, citing pollution as a major threat to public health, esthetics, and economic use of our water resources. These are still good reasons to be concerned about water pollution. Let us look, however, at the significant change which has taken place in the public health aspects of pollution.

In 1900 typhoid fever was the prevalent waterborne disease in Iowa and the nation. The coliform test—still our major indicator of the biological safety of water—was developed to serve as an indication of the presence or absence in water of bacterial organisms which inhabit the human intestinal tract. The test was and is used most successfully since the absence of coliforms indicates that bacterial disease organisms are also absent. Thus, if the coliform test is negative, we are almost certain that no typhoid organisms can survive.

Today, however, we are not concerned about waterborne bacterial diseases. Our problems now are with viral diseases. In 1953 there was a serious outbreak of infectious hepatitis in Des Moines which seemed to be centered in septic tank areas of the city. In 1961 there were 1,985 cases of hepatitis in Iowa while typhoid fever cases were almost non-existent. Recently, statistical studies have indicated that the incidence of hepatitis is higher in cities with higher levels of turbidity carried over into municipal water supplies after normal water treatment. In New Delhi, India, a few years ago over 50,000 cases of hepatitis were traced to a virus-contaminated water supply even though supposedly adequate water treatment was given to the grossly polluted source. "It can't happen here," we said; but from November, 1956–February, 1957, the same thing happened in Rhinebeck Township in New York. In 1965 engineers, scientists, medical doctors, and epidemiologists swarmed over Riverside, California, to determine how a waterborne epidemic of *Salmonella typhimurium* could result in a public water supply.

Waterborne epidemics still occur. Polio, hepatitis, Coxsackie, and some 86 Echo viruses are known to survive in sewage wastes and can be isolated from polluted water. Many of these are more resistant to chlorine destruction and removal in waste and water treatment than are bacterial pathogens or the "indicator" coliform organisms. Viruses are on the order of 100 times smaller than bacteria and will travel further and survive longer. The absence of coliforms today may indicate the absence of bacterial organisms but it does not indicate the absence of viral pathogens.

If that is true, you might ask, why have we not had more waterborne viral epidemics? Here again more information is required. Right now the consensus seems to be that the levels of virus in water are below the minimal infective dose (MID) required to produce infection in the majority of the population. Perhaps the susceptible people contract viral diseases from the public water supply, but epidemics only occur when the MID is exceeded. We need more information concerning such critical infective levels for the various waterborne pathogens.

Public health is also affected when toxic chemicals find their way into streams ultimately used for water supplies. The obviously toxic chemicals such as arsenics and cyanides must be excluded. However, these are not of as much concern as the many chemicals we know to be present in water but whose public health significance is unknown. For example, we know insecticides kill fish in streams but we have little knowledge of their long-term effect on humans. Actually, we lump all such dissolved organics into a catchall CCE (carbon chloroform extractables) test. In this test the water is passed through a carbon column which serves to extract an unknown fraction of the dissolved organics from the water. An unknown fraction of these organics is then extracted from the carbon by fluxing the carbon column with chloroform. The weight of the organics recovered from the water passed through the carbon is used as a measure of the concentration of the organics present. This concentration, though probably only qualitative, has been steadily increasing in many streams and public water supplies. Levels of 200–400 ppb are not uncommon. Although current drinking-water standards place a limit on the CCE levels, there is still no real knowledge of the public health significance of the many chemical compounds represented.

Although recognizing health as a factor of concern in stream pollution, the public is more concerned about the reaction of their senses to pollution—that is, esthetics. If they feel, see, or smell the presence of pollution, they become very concerned. We are a water-loving people and our recreation more and more is water based. We swim, boat, fish, water ski, and skin dive. If pollution interferes, we rightly become indignant. All of us can recognize the objectionable foul smell of hydrogen sulfide, the revolting sight of fecal material, the nuisance of floating debris, and the annoying oil stain on our boat. But how do you go about evaluating how much pollution is too much if it is less than that which affects our esthetics? People boat, swim, water ski, and skin dive in polluted water without apparent esthetic offense. How far back should we roll pollution? How do we evaluate the reduction of water use value against the cost of eliminating the pollution? Certainly we do not expect to return all our watercourses to "wild stream" status. This whole area requires much coordinated, interdisciplinary study so that decisions can be based on fact and not on desires only.

Pollution can also significantly increase the costs involved in subsequent uses made of polluted water. Pollution can increase the cost of treating water for municipal and industrial use by requiring additional treatment units and more degrees of treatment. In some rivers the presence of acids in the water have so corroded ships that they have had to abandon use of those rivers. Many fishing streams have been so polluted as to completely eliminate fishing industries. Typical examples are prevalent all over Iowa.

In 1961, for example, the Cedar River was so polluted that the taste and odor in the river water carried over into the public water supply. In an effort to reduce the taste and odor, the Cedar Rapids water plant spent about $1,000 extra per day for carbon and potassium permanganate. This represented more than four to five times the normal cost of water treatment chemicals. Although the water was safe to drink after such treatment, the taste and odor persisted and resulted in significant economic loss to the Quaker Oats plant and to bakeries when it began to appear in their products. A significant public health problem arose since hundreds, to escape the taste and odor, turned to alternate private water sources for drinking water. Many of these alternate supplies were found to be *unsafe.*

The 1961 Cedar River pollution also affected fishing in the river; the distinctive taste and odor tainted fish caught there. First reported in the headwaters, the tainted fish were reported further and further downstream as the pollution moved in that direction. At the time Waterloo caught most of the political heat for "polluting" the river, yet today we are still unable to say what caused the pollution, what steps to take to prevent a recurrence, and what to do to reduce the taste and odor in the treated water if it should occur again. We "think" *Actinomycetes,* an organism about which we know too little, was our problem maker, but we are not positive as to why. The wastes from Waterloo may have contributed to the problem but certainly did not cause it, since the taste and odor appeared first in fish far north of that city.

In another Iowa city we apparently have the first traces of fluoride and phosphate pollution beginning to appear in a water supply as a result of groundwater pollution from an industrial plant. In order to evaluate the potential of the problem, extensive studies using new techniques are indicated. How extensive is the damage? Can the water continue to be used indefinitely? If we halt the pollution, how long will it be before the pollution clears out of the underground aquifer? Is it cheaper to eliminate the pollution, to find a new source of water, or treat the polluted source?

In western Iowa both Omaha and Council Bluffs use the polluted Missouri River as a source of public water supply. Each spring runoff period brings taste and odor problems and a period of difficult water treatment. We might blame these occurrences on municipal or industrial pollution, but recent studies using X-ray diffraction techniques indicate they accompany a distinct change in the character of clay solids in the water. During difficult treatment periods the clays are primarily montmorillonite clays from Iowa's western hills rather than the kaolinite and quartzite clays from the Dakotas. Why the tastes and odors accompany the Iowa clays we do not yet know.

Undoubtedly, the major threat which gross organic pollution presents is the destruction of fish life in a stream. When raw or partially treated domestic or industrial wastes are discharged to the stream, the organic materials serve as a food supply for microorganisms. In consuming the new food supply, the microorganism will require the use of oxygen (the exact amount can be determined from the BOD test). The oxygen used by the biological activity can only be supplied by that available in solution in the stream. Unfortunately, nature provides a maximum of 9 pounds of oxygen per million pounds of water when the water is at 20°C. At higher temperatures, when biological activity is greater, it contains even less. Thus, if the oxygen demand of the waste is greater than the oxygen available in the stream or that which can be supplied to the stream by nature as the oxygen is used up, the oxygen level in the stream may be partially or completely depleted. Since fish too require oxygen, they will be affected by such oxygen depletions. Complete loss of oxygen means complete loss of fish, and odors result.

The task of the water pollution control specialist is to predict the present and future waste load and the critical stream flow and temperature conditions. With these data he can then design a treatment plant which will accomplish enough of the waste treatment so that the residual wastes discharged to the stream will never result in causing a nuisance or damaging conditions in the stream.

Occasionally, the treatment accorded a waste can alleviate one pollution condition and produce another. For example, in Madison, Wisconsin, the treatment of the domestic wastes convert the nitrogenous matter to nitrates. Discharged into local lakes, the nitrates served as ideal nutrients for algae growths and the lakes were soon clogged with a new problem. Extensive studies are under way in many places to determine new methods to be used in the economical elimination of such nutrients from treated wastes.

In Iowa problems are similar, but the nutrients (phosphates and nitrates) in streams occur primarily as a result of deliberate application of them on the land in agricultural chemicals and in fertilizers. Methods for keeping them on the soil and out of our streams need study. Of 185 fish kills in 1961 studied by the U.S. Public Health Service, 73 were caused by agricultural poisons, 57 by industrial discharges, 15 by municipal wastes, and 40 by miscellaneous causes.

All of these problems need continued study to determine methods of pollution elimination, pollution abatement, and pollution reduction. Ultimately, some problems will be solved and some will not. In the future, decisions must be made after careful consideration of several approaches to solution of pollution problems resulting from some specific wastes:

1. Prohibit their manufacture and use (ABS, insecticides)?
2. Treat water containing the waste at point of downstream use?
3. Completely eliminate the waste at the point of origin?
4. Abandon subsequent use of the water receiving the waste?

In most cases new methods of measuring the extent and effect of pollution and of eliminating it will need to be developed. To facilitate the development and adoption of such new techniques, the state water pollution control agency should proceed rapidly in setting stream and effluent standards for the waters in the state. If new processes are to be encouraged, however, the water pollution agency should not also dictate the physical installation required in treatment of a waste to meet that standard.

WHAT DO WE DO ABOUT POLLUTION?

In establishing a permissible stream quality standard, each potential constituent must be evaluated and classified into one of the previously discussed categories: (1) must be prohibited from the receiving water, (2) undesirable and should be prohibited, (3) permissible, and (4) desirable in the receiving water. Since the effects of a constituent will be concentration dependent, its assignment to one of these categories will be influenced both by its concentration in the raw waste and the level which can be achieved *economically* by treatment. Once a stream standard has been established, the engineer must design, construct, and provide for operation of treatment facilities whose effluent, when it reaches the stream, will meet the required stream standard.

Ultimately, liquid wastes are disposed of by discharging them into bodies of water or on or beneath the surface of the ground. Disposal into water is the most common and is referred to as disposal by dilution—the discharge of a raw waste or the effluent from a treatment plant into a body of water of sufficient size to prevent health, esthetic, or economic nuisances. Disposal on land is not common; disposal underground, commonly called groundwater recharge, is increasing for the purpose of restoring diminishing groundwater levels.

The methods of treatment used for altering the characteristics of liquid wastes fall into the following classifications: (1) preliminary treatments, (2) primary treatments, (3) secondary treatments, and (4) tertiary treatments. *Preliminary treatments* include those processes which do not significantly reduce the pollutional strength of a waste but which do serve to protect or prepare the waste for subsequent treatment by altering the waste characteristics. Coarse screening, grit removal, comminution, and preaeration are common preliminary treatment processes. *Primary treatments* include those processes which reduce the floating and suspended solids present in the wastes by mechanical means or by the action of gravity. Fine screens and sedimentation tanks are the common primary treatment processes. *Secondary treatments* depend on biological processes to reduce further the suspended and dissolved solids which are present in the liquid effluents from primary treatment. Trickling filter and activated sludge processes are typical secondary treatments. In general, the influent to secondary treatment has received primary treatment; the influent to a primary treatment may or may not have received preliminary treatment. If a waste has received both primary and secondary treatment it is considered to have received complete treatment.

Complete treatment, up to about 1965, used both primary and secondary processes to produce a plant effluent of the highest quality, supplemented occasionally by use of additional processes such as disinfection or intermittent sand filtration. However, it has become evident that municipal and industrial wastes now include many contaminants that are resistant to, or even totally unaffected by, conventional water and waste treatment processes. Such contaminants, called *refractory substances,* include both organic and inorganic materials and require *advanced waste treatment* or *tertiary treatment* processes for their removal. Adsorption, electrodialysis, extraction, foaming, and ion exchange are typical treatment processes being evaluated for separation of refractories from water and wastes. A major research effort is being made to adapt these methods for use in waste treatment.

In addition to treatments used for the separation of pollutants from the liquid stream, a number of processes are used for reducing the problem of disposing of the concentrated wastes, in the form of sludges, from both primary and secondary treatment processes. Such concentrated waste treatment processes include sludge concentration, digestion, filtration, drying, and incineration.

In adapting processes for the treatment of the liquid and solid portions of a sewage or industrial waste, the engineer must bear in mind the fact that it is impossible to destroy any of the chemical elements present. They can, however, be changed to produce different chemical substances than those present in the original waste. The design of a treatment plant, then, involves the provision of sufficient treatment processes for the economical conversion of waste constituents to forms which can be removed from the liquid portion by mechanical straining, sedimentation, gasification, or evaporation.

Disposal of sewage by dilution includes the discharge of a raw waste or treatment plant effluent into a body of water of sufficient size to prevent the creation of a nuisance or to protect the public health. The degree of dilution required will depend on the quality standard established for the receiving body of water and the volume and strength of the waste. No matter what dilution is provided, the forces of natural or self-purification inherent in the receiving body of water will, with time, help to return the water to its original state of biological equilibrium. Nature cannot, however, be expected to return the water to its original state of cleanliness if refractory contaminants are present in the waste discharge.

When untreated domestic sewages were discharged to large streams, the dilution required was estimated by rules of thumb based on experience. If the available dilution were inadequate, the sewage was treated to reduce the relative amount of putrescible matter present to that which could be adequately assimilated in the available dilution water.

Public interest in water pollution control has so increased that no untreated waste should ever be discharged to a receiving body of water. To prevent offense to the esthetic senses of man, all wastes should receive a minimum of primary treatment.

Preliminary treatment processes are designed either to protect subsequent treatment units or appurtenances in a water pollution control plant or to change the character of the wastes to improve the efficiency of subsequent treatment units. Such processes generally do not significantly alter the pollutional characteristics of the wastes in the treatment unit itself. The most common preliminary treatment processes include screening, comminuting, grit and detritus removal, and preaeration. Frequently, flow measuring devices are included as preliminary treatment units in a plant, but they are not directly involved as a treatment process.

The first step in the treatment of sewage or industrial waste is coarse screening. The screens or bar screens are designed to remove the larger particles of floating or suspended solids which might clog subsequent pumps or pipelines in the plant. Bar screens found early success but involved excessive labor for cleaning and the handling of the accumulated screenings. With time mechanically cleaned screens were developed. Later, grinders were added so that screenings could be reduced in size and returned to the sewage. The obvious next step involved the grinding of the larger solids without first having to remove them from the waste. Accordingly, comminutors and barminutors are now used extensively for this purpose.

Grit chambers are included in a treatment plant when the sewage contains significant quantities of sand or other inert matter in suspension. Significant amounts will be found when combined sewers, industrial wastes, or runoff from unpaved streets permit large quantities of such materials to enter the treatment plant. If allowed to enter the plant, such grit would tend to abrade pumps and valves and would occupy valuable volume in subsequent treatment units. Grit chambers are designed to remove the sand while most of the organic materials continue on through the plant.

Preaeration of raw sewage may be practiced to improve the removal of suspended solids in subsequent primary treatment units. Preaeration involves the addition of sufficient air to increase the dissolved oxygen and to flocculate the sewage so that it will settle more readily. Since almost all settleable solids are removed by sedimentation, the preaeration only slightly increases the proportion of the solids that are settleable but greatly increases the settling rate. Preaeration processes are most applicable where strong sewages are treated and where grit removal is also required.

To maintain a close record of waste volume passing through or bypassing a treatment plant, it is essential that flow measuring devices be provided in plant design. Ordinarily, the flow measuring device should immediately follow the bar screens so that bypassed wastes can be both screened and measured. However, measuring devices are desirable at many locations in the plant and can be located wherever convenient and economical.

Primary treatment of sewage involves the passage of raw or preaerated wastes through sedimentation or flotation tanks or through fine screens designed to remove the readily settleable material from suspension. Plain sedimentation tanks permit the solids to settle to the bottom; they are then moved from there to a central collection point for removal from the tank. To accelerate the settling process, inorganic or organic coagulant aids may be used to increase the size of the flocculent solids and the proportion of solids that will settle. Flotation tanks use widely dispersed bubbles of air to float the settleable suspended solids to the surface where they can be skimmed off. Fine screens may be used in place of sedimentation tanks to remove those suspended solids which can be strained out of the liquid readily. If the screens are made fine enough, their efficiency in solids removal will approach that of sedimentation.

Sewage and industrial wastes are given such primary treatment to reduce solids that would form sludge banks and unsightly conditions in the receiving body of water, to reduce the food available to microorganisms and the resultant depression of available dissolved oxygen in the river, and to prepare the sewage for additional treatment. Adequately designed, primary treatment units will generally remove from 98–99 per cent of the settleable solids, 60–80 per cent of suspended solids, and 30–50 per cent of the oxygen demand from a domestic waste. When a small city or town is located on a large river, primary treatment may be the only treatment required to protect the stream.

Primary treatment, in effect, uses the force of gravity to separate the raw sewage into a water component and a concentrated solids or sludge component. The water component will still contain significant amounts of dissolved and colloidal pollutants unaffected by primary treatment. The water component can be discharged or given further treatment to remove these residual pollutants. The sludge component, however, cannot be discharged to a watercourse and must be given further treatment to prevent the creation of a nuisance. The type of sludge treatment provided will depend on both economic considerations and the qualifications of the personnel available to operate the plant.

To dispose of the sludge properly, it must be further concentrated to reduce the volume to be handled. Ordinarily, domestic sewage sludge removed from primary treatment units will contain from 0.5 to 3.0 per cent solids. Several *sludge conditioning* processes can be used to concentrate the sludge to a level of 5 to 10 per cent solids. The sludge can be passed through sludge concentrator tanks, a type of sedimentation tank in which the sludge is gently mixed while settling. The liquid containing less solids at the top of the tank, called supernatant, is run back to the main liquid stream and the concentrated sludge at the bottom of the tank is drawn off for further treatment.

Probably the most widely used process for sludge conditioning is anaerobic digestion. This process depends on maintaining the sludge under conditions ideal for the conversion of the organic solids in the sludge to organic acids and to gas. This is accomplished by anaerobic microorganisms which serve to destroy a portion of the organic matter by converting it to methane, a useful gaseous product, and carbon dioxide. Digestion will serve to reduce the volume to be handled and will make the sludge more easily dewaterable.

Following conditioning, the sludge must usually be further dewatered, although in some cases it may be discharged to sludge lagoons where it is allowed to dewater naturally by seepage into the ground or by evaporation. The means used to dewater sludge from about 5 per cent solids to about 30–40 per cent solids are referred to as *primary sludge dewatering processes*. The most common of these involve the use of sand beds, mechanical filters, and centrifuges. The use of sand beds has been the most widely used method in Iowa. The sludge is run onto level sand beds to a depth of 10–12 inches. The sand beds are provided with an underdrain system which carries the liquid draining from the sludge back to the plant influent. After about two to three weeks of dewatering by draining and evaporation, the sludge can be removed from the sand bed.

Both raw and digested sludge can be given primary dewatering on mechanical filters, which are currently finding application for dewatering digested sludge in larger cities and in smaller installations where sludge is dewatered raw. Filters used include rotary vacuum filters with cloth, wire mesh, or coil spring filter media, and rotary concentrators using filter cloths made from synthetic materials.

Primary dewatered sludge can be disposed of by burial in a sanitary land fill or, if digested, it may be applied to land for use as a fertilizer or soil conditioner. Frequently, however, it will be desirable to reduce the moisture in sludge from the level of 60–70 per cent common in primary dewatered sludge to a level of from 10–20 per cent. The means used to accomplish this are referred to as *secondary sludge dewatering processes*. Such processes include the use of spray driers, rotary tunnel driers, and incinerators. In each case heat is supplied to the sludge to evaporate the undesired water and to destroy any pathogenic organisms which may remain viable. Use of secondary dewatering processes are economical where the dried product is to be used as fertilizer or where an ashed product must be produced to reduce the ultimate disposal problem.

The water component of domestic sewage which has received primary treatment will still contain about 20–40 per cent of its original content of suspended solids and from 50–70 per cent of its original oxygen demand. To further reduce these pollutants, the sewage may be given secondary treatment. *Secondary treatment processes* are biological processes in which the waste is passed through an environment where microorganisms can flourish and can remove suspended and dissolved pollutants by converting them to energy and additional biological cells. The pollutants actually serve as a food source for the microorganisms. Use of pollutants by biological life serves to convert them from solution and colloidal suspension to cells which can be removed from the liquid stream by sedimentation. In fact, nearly all secondary treatment units are followed by sedimentation units to remove the excess biological cells produced.

The most common secondary treatment includes the trickling filter and activated sludge processes. Both processes require a source of balanced food, atmospheric oxygen, and an environment suitable for the growth of microorganisms. In the trickling filter process the clarified primary effluent is allowed to trickle through a bed of crushed rock or other suitable media. The microbiological life is encouraged to grow in a biological slime which grows around the filter media. The media is designed to provide sufficient surface area for the growth of the required type and volume of organisms required in the treatment and sufficient void volume to permit the passage of liquid wastes and air. All oxygen requirements are obtained by the intimate contact between the liquid waste and air in the bed. The biological life removes the pollutants from the liquid waste, by adsorption and absorption during its passage through the bed, and subsequently completes its conversion to energy and new cells after the liquid waste has passed through the plant. Both standard-rate and high-rate filters are commonly used; the difference in the two types being dependent chiefly on the rate at which liquid and organic wastes are added to the filter and the amount of recirculation of the trickling effluent returned to the trickling filter influent. In this process the biological life essentially remains fixed in one place and the food material required to sustain this life is carried to it in the liquid waste stream.

In the activated sludge process the liquid waste is brought into intimate contact with the required biological life and oxygen in an aeration tank. The waste containing the food, or pollutional material, enters the aeration tank at the same rate it enters the plant. The biological life required to assimilate the food contained in the waste is added with the raw or settled waste in the form of a return-activated sludge. The return-activated sludge constitutes that portion of the biologically active sludge from the aeration tank which is removed from the liquid in a final sedimentation tank and ultimately returned to the aeration tank. The oxygen requirements of the mixed liquor, consisting of waste and activated sludge, is supplied by introducing air into the aeration tank, using diffused air or mechanical aeration devices. Oxygen in the air will go into solution and be used in the metabolism of the food in the waste. The activated sludge process involves many variations and utilizes many different types of aeration tanks and aeration equipment. In each case, however, the biological life in the activated sludge moves through the aeration tank with the waste flow. The amount of return sludge and aeration provided is determined by the volume and strength of the waste and the particular process variation in use.

Secondary treatment processes can be designed to provide overall plant removals of 90–95 per cent of the suspended solids and oxygen demand present in the raw waste. The economics involved in secondary treatment will determine which of the two main processes and which process variation will be used in a particular waste treatment installation. Secondary treatments are required where the standards of permissible pollution established for the receiving stream would be exceeded by the discharge of wastes receiving only primary treatment. With increase in population and in use and reuse of water, the standards for permissible pollution to be established for receiving bodies of water will become more and more restrictive. Some contaminants are resistant to or are totally unaffected by the most modern conventional water and waste treatment processes. Such contaminants (*refractories*) call for the development of advanced waste treatment processes, or tertiary processes, that can be used to alleviate a water pollution problem or to renovate waste water for direct or deliberate reuse. Depending on the particular problem, advanced waste treatment may be provided as a final stage of treatment in the water pollution control plant to remove the contaminant from the total waste stream. In some cases, however, where the contaminant affects only one subsequent use, the tertiary treatment process may be included as part of a subsequent water treatment plant. The proper place to provide refractory removal will depend on the economics and control required in the particular application.

Almost any physical or chemical process for the separation of a soluble material from a solvent can be adapted for advanced waste treatment. Processes under evaluation include adsorption, electrodialysis, emulsion separation, evaporation, extraction, foaming, freezing, hydration, ion exchange, and chemical or electrochemical oxidation. Such advanced treatment processes seek to provide complete removal of a specific refractory component or the removal of suspended solids and oxygen demand to a level of 99.9 per cent or more.

CHAPTER 3

ECONOMICS OF WATER QUALITY

JOHN F. TIMMONS

OUR NATURAL RESOURCES INCLUDING AIR, SOIL, AND WATER CONSTITUTE basic foundations for our economic growth and natural strength. At the same time our economy uses these resources as its "garbage pails" into which technological wastes are cast, either inadvertently or purposely. These wastes or "fallouts" emanate from the chemical, biological, mechanical, and nuclear processes which make our advanced and complex economy function. But they bring significant quality changes in our air, soil, and water resources which threaten continued economic growth. These wastes which pollute our natural resources are serious throughout the state and nation today and may well become progressively more serious in the years ahead as our economy strives to satisfy the diversified and increasing demands of our growing population at higher per capita levels of living.

This chapter is limited to economic considerations of water quality in addition to water *quality* as contrasted with water *quantity* considerations, if indeed the two concepts can logically be separated. Effects of wastes and pollution on air, soil, and other natural resources and analytical interactions between water and other resources in terms of alternative waste disposals and side effects on these other resources are not evaluated here.

The major purpose of this chapter is to identify and articulate water quality problems within an economic framework for (1) maxi-

JOHN F. TIMMONS is professor of economics, Iowa State University, Ames, Iowa. The author is indebted to Merwin D. Dougal, assistant professor of civil engineering, and Ed Seay, research assistant in economics, both of Iowa State University, for their helpful criticism of an earlier draft of this chapter.

mizing the satisfaction of human wants from the use of water and (2) minimizing the costs of producing these satisfactions, considering both the direct as well as derived demands for water including the goods and services water helps produce.[1] A second purpose is to elaborate an economic framework within which water quality problems facing our state and nation may be analyzed in the quest for solutions to these problems. In pursuing these objectives, investigation is made into the nature of and the growing demand for water and the economic dimension of water quality problems in relation to physical and structural dimensions, supply and demand characteristics, use interrelationships, and costs and benefits associated with particular uses and use methods.

Before proceeding further, however, the terms water quality, pollution, and control should be defined. *Water quality* means the properties of water which influence its use. These properties are affected by both nature and man. Natural quality of water varies with the season of the year; climate; geographical location; and the kinds of rocks, soil, air, organic material, and organisms through which water passes and with which it interacts. *Pollution* means man's activities which degrade the natural quality of water. But pollution is a matter of both kind and degree and must be related to uses of the water by man. This means that both quality and pollution must be evaluated in terms of the uses to be made of water, including its use for transporting and receiving waste discharges. Thus, the relevant issue appears to involve what levels of quality are consistent with the maximization of man's satisfactions from the use of water both presently and in the future. By *control,* we mean public intervention to achieve and/or maintain levels of water quality necessary for satisfying man's wants in his use of water resources within the context of maximization.

ECONOMIC NATURE OF WATER QUALITY PROBLEMS

In 1965 usage of water in the United States was estimated to exceed 320 billion gallons per day.[2] By 1980 this demand may well double. This would mean an annual increase of around 6 per cent which would represent an annual allowance for a population growth of around 1.5 per cent per year and a per capita increase of around 4.5 per cent per year. However, such aggregate estimates must be redefined in terms of water quality since particular uses of water require specific quality characteristics. As Samuel Taylor Coleridge put it, there may be "water, water, every where/Nor any drop to drink." The problem arises in terms of the availability of a particular water quality needed for a particular use.

The nature of the water quality problem may be stated in terms of three general types of situations. First, wastes or pollution emanating from a particular use may foreclose other uses with an equal or even higher value. Costs of remedying the effects of quality pollutants may be prohibitive to the other use or uses.

Second, pollutants dumped into watercourses or other water supplies as a side effect or discharged as a treated waste of one use, may increase the cost of (or correspondingly decrease the benefits to) another use. And further, if these costs (including decreased benefits) affecting the second use were assessed back to the first cost, the resulting costs to the first use would exceed the benefits to the second use. Or, the benefits from a second use could be obtained in another manner at a lower cost. For example, a municipality with primary and secondary treatment leaves the water at a quality level inferior for use in downstream recreation, i.e., swimming. However, an off-stream impoundment which would provide the recreational use could be constructed at a cost less than the tertiary or third order treatment by the municipality.

Third, future extension of a particular use to meet increasing future demands may be prevented by excessive costs or permitted only by higher costs involved in abatement processes. For example, assume a manufacturing plant had been dumping treated industrial wastes (which still carried residual toxics) into a stream. Further, assume a downstream city which in the course of its growth had fully exploited its groundwater supply through wells and had to shift to stream water for its continued growth and development. Either the upstream plant would have to remove certain residual toxics or the municipality would have to treat the influent. The latter costs could prove prohibitive. The former costs could be borne by the upstream plant in removing the residual toxics as part of their processing at a lesser cost than would be involved if the municipality undertook the treatment. Hence, the municipality could afford to pay the plant for improving the water quality needed for the continued growth and expansion of the city.

Water quality is rapidly becoming recognized as strategic in the economic development of communities, states, and the nation. Communication media and private as well as public and quasipublic organizations are devoting increasing attention to water quality and water pollution problems. Most of the states have enacted some type of water quality control legislation. In June, 1965, the Iowa Water Pollution Control Act became law.[3] Under this act, ". . . it is hereby declared to be the public policy of this state to conserve the waters of the state and to protect, maintain, and improve the quality thereof for public water supplies, for the propagation of wildlife, fish, and aquatic life, and for domestic, agricultural, industrial, recreational, and other legitimate (beneficial) uses; to provide that no waste be discharged into any waters of the state without first being given the degree of treatment necessary to protect the legitimate (beneficial) uses of such waters; to provide for the prevention, abatement, and control of new, increasing, potential, or existing water pollution. . . ."

In the implementation, administration, and future amending of the Iowa law, the concept "degree of treatment" will necessarily have to be determined. Also, the public policy declaration to protect, maintain, and improve water quality will necessarily have to be applied to the uses enumerated in the act plus other uses. In the process difficult decisions will be called for when uses compete with each other for waters of particular qualities. It remains doubtful that our existing knowledge is sufficient to make such decisions if they are to result in maximizing the aggregate and variable components of satisfactions which are demanded by our society from water.

In October, 1965, President Johnson signed the federal Water Pollution Control Act which represents another step in a series of recent federal legislation dealing with water quality.[4] In signing this legislation, President Johnson forecast that additional legislation would be required to safeguard and upgrade water quality as needed for the economic growth and development of the nation. Similar questions raised above concerning the Iowa act may also be raised concerning federal legislation.

PHYSICAL, ECONOMIC, AND STRUCTURAL INTERRELATIONSHIPS

In the process of understanding and correcting water quality problems, it may be useful to regard water quality within a three-dimensional framework.[5] These dimensions are physical (including technological) economic, and structural (including institutional). The physical dimension is concerned with what is physically or technologically possible. Physical sciences are dedicated to and responsible for extending the range of physical possibilities and ascertaining the probabilities of consequences attached to particular water uses with pollution control measures. These responsibilities are discharged through technological discoveries and inventions. Although the continual expansion of physical possibilities is necessary for continued economic progress, technology in and by itself does not permit choice nor reveal the economic consequences of particular choices. The range of choice is broadened through physical studies, but making of decisions by individuals and public entities necessitates inquiries into the economic dimension which is dedicated to and responsible for revealing which physical or technical possibilities are economically feasible.

For example, physically or technologically, saline water can be changed into fresh water through desalinization processes. Water can be removed from salt through heating and freezing processes and salt can be removed from water through electrodialysis. A distillation plant at Freeport, Texas, converts sea water to fresh water at a cost of $1 per 1,000 gallons. An electrodialysis plant at Buckeye, Arizona, converts saline water to fresh water at $.33 per 1,000 gallons. Current costs of municipal water supplies drawn from aquifers and reservoirs run around $.25 per 1,000 gallons for water of comparable quality. Until the costs of desalinization are reduced through further technological refinements to where the costs of water produced are competitive with other water supplies or until the demand for water increases price to a point which will justify the cost, desalinization processes will remain largely physically possible but not economically feasible. Of course, in isolated instances such as islands, ships at sea, and arid lands without fresh water supplies, these desalinization processes have become competitive.

The economic dimension is necessary in making decisions about (1) levels of water quality and (2) the technological means for achieving particular water quality changes. Whether these levels are economically feasible depends upon consumers' wants as expressed in terms of prices, preferences, and the votes or decisions of their representatives in public legislative or administrative entities to whom the consumers have entrusted their decisions on preferences.

Even though a level of water quality and the technological means of achieving or maintaining it may be economically feasible, a third dimension is essential in the decision-making process. This third dimension is structural (or institutional), made up of laws and other group controls over individual behavior. These structures at a particular time and place may either (1) inhibit or (2) facilitate the realization of levels of water quality which are both physically possible and economically feasible.

These structures (or institutions) provide the "rules of the game" in the use or misuse of water. They provide for public intervention when necessary to protect the public interest. They determine what is permissible at a particular time and place and under particular conditions as related to particular uses.

Thus, water quality must be analyzed within the three-dimensional framework in terms of three questions: What is physically possible? What is economically feasible? What is structurally permissible? Only through the answers to these three questions can unified decisions be made and enforced which will insure optimal water quality and maximum net benefits from its use.

SUPPLY AND DEMAND CHARACTERISTICS

Both the quality of available water supplies and quality of water demanded by particular uses are extremely varied. There are two fundamental characteristics of the supply of and demand for water insofar as quality is concerned. These are (1) quality heterogeneity of water supplies and (2) quality differentiation of demand according to uses.

Quality Heterogeneity of Water Supplies

A particular supply unit of water may be hard or soft, warm or cool, colored or clear, or it may vary in many other ways. The common chemical formula for water, H_2O, has tended to impute a homogeneity to water which actually does not exist. During the forties, fifties, and sixties the structure of water has been complicated by the discovery of three isotypes for both hydrogen and oxygen which results in mixtures of thirty-three different substances. Thus, water is not a simple single compound but is extremely complicated. Actually, "less is known about water than about many other liquids" according to a recent report.[6]

Water has many unusual properties which vary among existing supplies and condition its use. Water occurs in three distinct forms: solid, liquid, and gas. Water expands when frozen while most substances contract and has a very high heat capacity and surface tension. Also, water easily dissolves many compounds which thereafter remain in solution thus earning for water the title "universal solvent." Water quality varies tremendously through impurities which are introduced by natural as well as man-made forces. Thus, various water sources possess different qualities which must be appraised in terms of the use to which a particular source of water is to be put.

Quality Differentiation of Demand for Water

A supply of water with a particular quality may serve a number of purposes unequally well. Different uses demand different properties in water or at least vary in their toleration of particular properties. For example, living cells may require the presence of certain minerals in water, whereas battery cells will not tolerate minerals. Quality of water must necessarily be associated with a particular use. Different qualities are required (or tolerated) for human consumption, navigation, power, irrigation, food processing, manufacturing, air conditioning, recreation, and fish and wildlife propagation. Even within each of these major categories specialized demands require different water qualities. Within the recreational use, swimming, fishing, and boating possess quality differentiations. Within manufacturing, beer, aluminum, paper, and synthetic fiber production possess important quality differentiations.

Thus, the "quality mix" of a particular water supply must be appraised in terms of the uses to which it is put. Water quality suited for one use may be absolutely unsuited for another use. For instance, navigation purportedly can tolerate the lowest quality mix, requiring basically only a water surface and adequate depth. It appears that there is little if any relevancy for a universal quality standard. On the other hand, quality standards must be developed in relation to the specific uses to be made of particular water supplies in the process of satisfying specific human wants.

WATER QUALITY USE RELATIONSHIPS

Three types of relationships between water uses may be identified. These relationships are relevant in setting quality standards and in making allocations of water among uses as well as in fixing charges against particular uses. These relationships are (1) neutral, (2) complementary, and (3) competitive.

Neutral relationships between uses of water exist when one use has no effect on the quality of other uses. An example would be use of water in a major river both for navigation and for receiving effluent discharge from a factory. We will assume that neither use impairs the other; that is, the relationship between the two uses is neutral. The navigation use would not affect the quality of water or amount of water available to the factory. On the other hand, the nonconsumptive use of the water by the factory, including its effluent discharge, would not restrict or alter in any way the navigation use. Therefore, each use would be neutral to the other and no decisions on water quality would be called for in proceeding with both.

Complementary relationships arise when one use upgrades the water quality for the second use without the second degrading the water for the first. Therefore, the first use complements the quality for the second use. An example would be the uses of water for swimming and for air conditioning where only temperature is altered. In using the water for cooling, the water would absorb heat which would improve the temperature for swimming except, of course, when water temperature would already equal or exceed the optimum. Another example of complementary uses would consist of an upstream plant which used large amounts of water for cooling with its effluent consequently warming the downstream waters. In this instance the downstream plant which we assume requires warm water, would benefit from the use made of the water by the upstream plant. In the case of complementary quality uses as with neutral quality uses, no decisions are called for in proceeding with both uses because no conflicts exist.

Competitive relationships between quality uses, on the other hand, arise when one use conflicts with another use or uses. If the upstream plant mentioned above warms the water to the degree that brook trout would not survive downstream, a competitive relationship between the plant use of water for cooling and the fishing use would arise and a decision would be required in resolving the conflict. The competitive relationships between uses are the core of water quality problems. These problems demand decisions to enable the conflicts arising from competitive uses to be resolved.

IDENTIFYING AND ACHIEVING OPTIMUM WATER QUALITY BY VARIOUS USES[7]

The following issues are central to understanding and resolving problems arising from conflicting and competitive uses of water:

1. What quality standards for particular supplies of water are to be achieved and/or maintained?
2. What are the criteria for allocating water of various qualities among competing uses?
3. What are the technological possibilities for achieving and maintaining a particular quality standard?
4. Which alternative technological possibility is economically superior?
5. How may the costs and benefits of achieving and maintaining quality standards be assigned among users?
6. What structures in the form of laws, agencies, and administrative procedures are needed to implement the answers to the above questions?

The Public Optimum

In working out the answers to these questions, it appears helpful to begin with a consideration of the public optimum of water quality and the allocation of this water among uses and users that will result in the maximum satisfaction of people's wants over time. This involves the production of the total variety and amount of goods and services that people want at the lowest possible per unit cost.

Insofar as decision makers (and their constituents) are interested in maximizing the net value product of water and other resources, economics provides guides and criteria for evaluating various alternative legal and technological means for accomplishing the objective. Thus, from a public viewpoint, the maximization of long-run social benefit from the use of water resources may appropriately represent a public objective of water use. This is true insofar as people prefer more to less of the goods and services obtainable from the use of water and other resources. To the extent that this is a public objective, economic criteria may guide physical and legal measures for affecting water use. Historically and generally this process has been the reverse. Physical means of control have been initiated or laws have been passed or court decisions have been rendered that may not be consistent with the maximum satisfaction of wants over time.

An initial problem in allocation of water involves determination of the quality and amount of water that can be used economically at a particular time and place for each competing use. From such an analysis of all competing uses the aggregate demand for water may be estimated and allocation criteria may be developed.

Obviously, water use cannot be isolated from use of other resources that are its technical complements. Water is rapidly becoming a scarce resource in an economic sense, giving rise to the need for economic decisions for its use; but equally important are decisions relative to the use of labor and capital which are also scarce resources.

Figure 3.1 illustrates the amount of water for a particular use in relation to the costs and value product involved. The total quantity of water used is shown on the X axis; the total value of product resulting from use of the various amounts of water in a particular use (Use I) is shown on the Y axis. The outlay curve for water of a particular quality used is represented by ABE, i.e., outlay Curve I, while the total value of products from Use I is represented by CDE. Three points in the possible scale of use are shown on the total value product curve. C is the point at which the ratio of increase in total value product to increase in total outlay is greatest. Point D is the use of water at which the gross value product exceeds outlay by the maximum amount. Point E is the use of water at which the gross value product equals the total outlay.

If the use of water were terminated at point C, the rate of value product accrual per unit of outlay would be at a maximum but the full economic possibilities of water in Use I would not be realized since additional segments of water could be used for which value product would exceed the outlay involved. At point D the added outlay for the last increment of value product is just equal to the added value product resulting from this increment of outlay. At this point $25 of total outlay would result in $40 of total value product. The total value product exceeds the total outlay by a maximum of $15. Extension of outlay beyond this point would involve increments of outlay in excess of the value product added by such increments. This extension is not economically justifiable. (If we take our example from the public sector, we must assume that all [social] benefits and costs have been incorporated into the cost and revenue functions.)

Although the ratio of total value product to total outlay is unity

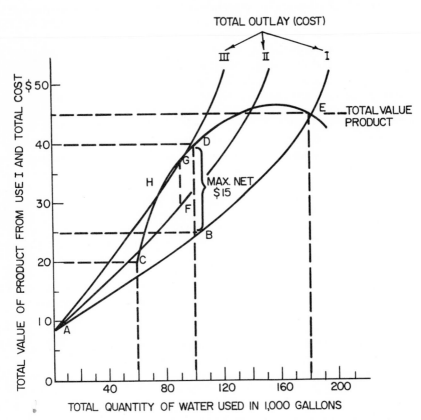

Fig. 3.1. Productive value of water in Use I related to cost of use.

or more between points D and E, the increments of value product resulting from the corresponding increments of outlay are increasingly less than the outlay for these respective increments of value product. Hence, the extension of use of water beyond point D is not economically justified. These increments of water (beyond point D) should be either diverted to another use or left unused.

From this illustration a basic principle of marginal analysis may be restated as follows: The amount of water allocated to a particular use should be extended to the point where marginal outlay (cost) equals marginal value product (revenue). Through the application of this principle to each of the many competing uses of water, an aggregate demand may be approximated for water use. Such estimates would, of course, change with the price per unit of product produced and the cost of units of water used. Thus, the application of the principle would embrace changes in consumer demand from the price side as well as changes in technology from the supply side. Such changes can readily be accommodated in the model presented.

Attention now turns from the amount of water that can be economically absorbed in one use (Use I on Figure 3.1) to the allocation of a given amount of water among several competing uses. Figure 3.2A provides a conceptual illustration of this problem and the possible solution. The underlying assumptions in this model are (1) a given supply of water and (2) two alternative competing uses for the given supply. For purposes of presenting the idea, only two competing uses are shown, although numerous alternative uses may be competing for the use of a given supply of water.

The budgeting curve AE shows all possible allocations to two uses of a given supply of water. The entire supply could be placed in Use I. This extreme allocation of the given water supply to Use I would be represented by point A. Another alternative allocation would be point E, wherein use of the entire water supply would be allocated to Use II. Besides these extreme allocations of water, many possible combinations of uses could be selected. For example, we could produce much of Use I and little of Use II, as at a point B; much of Use II and little of Use I, as at a point D; half of Use I and half of Use II, as at C; or any other of the many combinations along the budgeting curve AE. But which one of these many alternative combinations is the optimum?

The answer cannot be given until we are able to place values on the products. The selection of alternative uses should be in terms of a flexible choice criterion reflecting the changing desires of people. The choice criterion normally employed in specifying how resources should be used is the pricing mechanism. Profit is at a maximum if the rate of substitution among products (resource uses) is equal to the product price ratio. That is, the substitution or sacrifice ratio among production

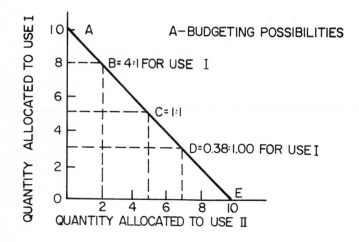

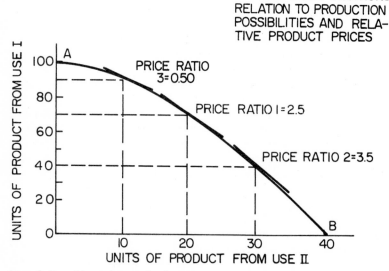

Fig. 3.2. Hypothetical allocations of a given supply of water between competing uses.

possibilities must be equal to the price ratio, the choice criterion applied by the society of consumers.

This principle is illustrated in Figure 3.2B. Suppose that from a given supply of one resource (such as water) or a given supply of a bundle of resources (such as water, capital, and labor) the following combination of products can be produced: all of commodity (or service) I and none of II; 90 of I and 10 of II; 70 of I and 20 of II, etc., as illustrated by curve AB in Figure 3.2B. The production possibility curve presents the sacrificial relationships. For example, in a change from a combination of 100 of I and none of II, to 90 of I and 10 of II, we sacrifice one unit of the former for each one unit gain in the latter. Under a third combination wherein 70 of I and 20 of II are produced, two units of I are lost for each one of II gained. Under a fourth combination 40 of I and 30 of II are produced, resulting in a gain of one unit of II for each 3 units of I given up. Generally, increased diversion of water for one use entails increasing sacrifices in other uses to the degree that water is scarce in relation to total demand.

Now suppose the consuming society wishes both products I and II, but that it places a price on the product of Use II that is 2.5 times the price of the product from Use I (Figure 3.2B). This price ratio, a price for product II that is 2.5 times the price of product I, is the choice criterion, the expression of relative importance by the consuming society that serves to indicate the optimum use of resources. The firm producing the product can increase profits by extending Use II at the expense of Use I as long as the substitution ratio of Use II for Use I (i.e., the amount of Use I sacrificed to gain one more unit of Use II) is less than the price ratio, expressed in terms of the quotient of price of Use II divided by price of Use I.

Hence, since the substitution or sacrifice ratio between the first two combinations of uses is only 1, and is less than the price ratio of 2.5, the second combination is preferable to the first (Figure 3.2B). The third combination (70 of I and 20 of II) also is preferable to the second since the substitution ratio of 2.0, in going between the second and third combinations, is still less than the price ratio of 2.5. However, the fourth combination is not preferable to the third, since the relative amount of I sacrificed to gain one more unit of II is more than proportional to the greater weight placed on Use II by consumers.

Note how we introduce the effects of changes in water quality into the analysis. Referring back to Figure 3.1, let us assume that outlay curve I represents the total cost of supplying varying quantities of water of the minimum quality needed for Use I (which might be swimming). If the supply of water available to swimming were not of the quality implied by outlay curve I, but rather of an inferior quality, additional treatment would be necessary to make the water supply suitable for the desired use. Additional costs would be attached to the increased amount of treatment. Such an increase in costs may be represented by a steeper total cost curve such as II. Two results are apparent from this change. First, the difference between the total value product and the total outlay has been reduced (from BD to FG). Second, the economically justifiable quantity of water used has been reduced from 100,000 gallons to 90,000 gallons. It is evident that if pollution with its attending costs continued to worsen, the cost curve would continue to rise until the situation illustrated by outlay curve III was reached. Here the maximum net difference between total value product and total outlay is zero, as indicated by point H. Obviously, if cost rose still higher, i.e., the cost curve was to the left of curve III, the use would be abandoned since costs would be greater than benefits received at every point.

The adverse effects ("costs") of pollution can also be illustrated by means of Figure 3.2. We might assume that Uses I and II lie on the same stream, with Use I upstream to II. If the effluent from Use I were polluted so as to make the waters of the stream unsuitable for Use II, society would be precluded from having the desired Use II under the existing price structure. In terms of the graphs of Figure 3.2, the budget line of part A and the production possibility curve of part B becomes identical with the vertical axis, OA. Under these circumstances the substitution ratio of Figure 3.2B is infinite (and greater than the price ratio).

Hence, a general principle has been indicated. It is necessary to determine the production possibilities in the use of water and determine the rate at which one use must be sacrificed to allow attainment of another use. Then these production possibilities and sacrifice (or substitution) ratios must be related to the relative importance that consumers attach to the different uses.

The Private Optimum

In a free-enterprise market economy, it has been assumed that private optimum and the public optimum would agree. Under this assumption markets would have to be fully competitive. Both consumers and producers would be attempting to maximize their net benefits. Factor contributors would (1) be rewarded for the productivity of their contributions and (2) bear the full costs of their actions in the production process. Each productive resource would be used to the point where the cost of an additional unit would equal its value product. Both costs and benefits would be borne fully by the productive unit or firm. This would include the full cost of treating water as both influent and effluent. Thus, available resources would be allocated by the market system in a manner that would maximize the satisfaction of everyone involved in the production and consumption processes.

Seldom, however, does the economic system function according to the assumptions and criteria specified above. Public intervention is frequently required to validate these assumptions and criteria. This is particularly true in the use of water which has been regarded as a free resource and has not been readily priced through the market. We shall proceed to identify the conditions which tend to prevent the market economy from functioning in an optimal manner. These conditions may be defined in terms of (1) dissociations of costs from benefits between private firms and between public and private sectors, (2) dissociations of benefits from costs between private firms and between public and private sectors, and (3) identification and measurement of costs and benefits with their respective incidences.[8]

Dissociation of costs from benefits[9]

In the use of water by private or by public firms external diseconomies frequently arise among competing uses whereby part of the costs of use are shifted to other firms (independent economic units) in a (1) spatial or (2) temporal incidence. Through this dissociation problems arise whereby certain water quality costs of one use are transferred to other water uses. Therein subsequent water uses are made more expensive or thereby other uses are foreclosed entirely. For example, the effluent discharged by a private or public firm, such as a municipality or a dairy product processing plant, would change the quality of the water to the extent that fishing or swimming uses downstream (spatial dissociation) would be precluded or the costs of restoring the quality that would support fishing or swimming downstream would be (1) prohibitive or (2) greater than would be the costs of treating the effluent before it is discharged into the stream by the municipality or dairy plant.

Dr. Allen Kneese has concluded that "a society that allows waste dischargers to neglect the offsite costs of waste disposal will not only devote too few resources to the treatment of waste but will also produce too much waste in view of the damage it causes."[10]

This type of dissociation may be interspatial or intertemporal in the sense that the costs are transferred either to other geographical areas or to future points in time.

Dissociation of benefits from costs

Benefits may be shifted from costs incurred by water users in making investments which yield a water quality also required by other uses. If the investor in water quality cannot capture the benefits required to provide the incentive to make the investment, he may be compensated by users who receive the benefit. Presumably, a surplus of benefits would be created which would constitute a base for compensation. Or users could be organized into investment groups who would share the costs in relation to benefits received from the water quality investments. The formation of a water quality district would be an application of this concept.

Measurement and incidence of benefits and costs[11]

In the process of determining the amount and incidence of costs and benefits associated with uses affecting or affected by water quality changes, the problem of measurement arises. For example, what is the worth of 100 fish or ducks killed by pollution in terms of hunting and fishing uses foregone? Obviously, since hunting and fishing are wants of man, loss of fish and game constitutes costs. But how can the costs be measured? Can cardinal or ordinal measurements be obtained? If not, possibly consumer preference studies could be performed which would array human preferences for various uses. Or the ballot votes of consumers or their legislative representatives may be used as expressions of preferences in lieu of the pricing mechanism.

A word of caution should be stated about the alternative to proceeding with restrictive legislation or other water quality control measures without identifying and measuring water quality benefits and costs of particular uses and of uses foregone or foreclosed. In such cases values are necessarily assigned inferentially to uses as consequences of the application of legislation and administration. For example, the requirement of an industrial plant to purify its effluent emptied into a stream at a level of quality which would cost the plant $100,000 and as a consequence would save 1,000 fish that otherwise would have perished would assign a value of $100 per fish. Or, the water quality standard requirement of $100,000 cost to a $1 million annual product industrial plant which would drive out the plant, would mean that the 1,000 fish would exceed the value of the plant. It would appear preferable to endeavor to ascertain the amount and incidences of benefits and costs before fixing quality standards, even though the values are extremely difficult to measure, than to proceed with measures which yield consequences that are not consonant with consumer preferences as expressed in prices or in consumer ballots directly or through their representatives in legislative or administrative capacities. At least, the consequences of particular water quality standards can be approximated, certainly in terms of cost and probably in terms of benefits, as data for decision making in relation to maximizing human satisfactions.

SUMMARY AND CONCLUSIONS

In summary we conclude that economic development of communities, states, and the nation multiplies the demand for water and at the same time expands the volume of waste materials reaching our water supplies. Even though the transport and dilution of wastes and potential recovery from biodegradable waste are valuable attributes of water, the effects of this use of water must be analyzed in terms of other uses to which the water may be put. In this regard water supplies as well as water demands are varied in terms of water quality.

In the enactment and administration of pollution control legislation water quality stream and groundwater and waste discharge standards must be set. The setting of such standards involves economic analyses of costs and benefits of alternative uses and the identification and measurement of their respective incidences. Such analysis could use the supply-demand units of water whether these units may be streams, aquifers, or some other common sources of supply from which conflicting demand may be satisfied.

In determining water quality standards by supply-demand units, it appears that much more information and analysis is needed including the technological, legal, and economic aspects. Concomitant with water quality standard determination is the need for water allocation among uses which yield the highest amount of goods and services in satisfying human wants. Coincident with this allocation is the problem of determining the incidences of costs and benefits in a manner that requires each use to bear its full costs which may otherwise be shifted over space and time. This full cost must consider water quality costs of treating water from influent points, through the production process or specific uses, and finally through waste treatment to the effluent discharge points for all uses over space and time for any specified water source and use region.

NOTES

1. For a discussion of water quantity problems, see John F. Timmons, "Problems in Water Use and Control," *Iowa Law Review*, Vol. 41, No. 2 (Winter, 1956), pp. 160–80.
2. H. A. Swenson and H. L. Baldwin, *A Primer on Water Quality*, (Washington, D.C., USGPO, 1965), p. 22.
3. Acts, 1965, Sixty-first General Assembly, Regular Session, State of Iowa, p. 436.
4. Public Law 89-234, Eighty-ninth Congress, S. 4, 1965.
5. For further reference to this concept, see Chap. 10, "Land Institutions Impeding and Facilitating Agricultural Adjustment" in *Problems and Policies of American Agriculture* (Ames, Iowa, Iowa State Univ. Press, 1959).
6. Swenson and Baldwin, p. 3.
7. For a further discussion of ideas presented in this section, see John F. Timmons, "Theoretical Considerations of Water Allocation Among Com-

peting Uses and Users," *Jour. of Farm Econ.*, Vol. 38, No. 5 (1956), pp. 1244–58.

8. See J. R. Hicks, *Value and Capital* (London, Oxford Univ. Press, 1950) and M. W. Rider, *Studies in the Theory of Welfare Economics* (New York, Columbia Univ. Press, 1947). Also see I. M. D. Little, *A Critique of Welfare Economics* (London, Oxford Univ. Press, 1958).

9. For a further development of ideas in this section, see John F. Timmons, "Integration of Law and Economics in Analyzing Agricultural Land Use Problems," *Jour. of Farm Econ.* Vol. 38, No. 5 (1955), pp. 1126–42.

10. Allen V. Kneese, *The Economics of Regional Water Quality Management* (Baltimore, The Johns Hopkins Press, 1964), p. 43.

11. Richard H. Leftwich, *The Price System and Resource Allocation* (New York, Rinehart, 1960), particularly Ch. 15.

CHAPTER 4

LEGAL AND REGULATORY ASPECTS OF WATER POLLUTION CONTROL

N. WILLIAM HINES

THE LATE LEGAL PHILOSOPHER KARL LEWELLYN ONCE SAID ". . . IF THE law of the state be seen as in the first essence not a 'code' nor a body of rules but as in first instance a growing institution, it opens itself at once to inquiry by the nontechnician."[1] Nowhere is this proposition truer than in the area of water pollution control.

As the water polution problem has grown in physical magnitude and its social and economic implications have attracted greater concern, so too has the body of law affecting it expanded. In the last half-century the law relating to pollution of our water resources has grown from a few vague common law principles and public health statutes to a complex and comprehensive panoply of federal, state, and local regulations.

ECONOMIC CONSIDERATION

If the law is understood as a living, growing institution that mirrors the particular anxieties of a society, it is not surprising that expansion in the knowledge of and concern about the state of our water resources should be accompanied by a proliferation in the legal controls relating to water pollution. It is the purpose of this chapter to trace the development of these legal controls of water quality and, where appropriate, to appraise the efficacy of particular types of regulation.

N. WILLIAM HINES is associate professor, College of Law, University of Iowa, Iowa City, Iowa.

PRIVATE CONTROLS

The earliest restraints on the pollution of waters were those created by the common law rights and duties recognized among individual water users. Under the so-called riparian system of water rights that was transplanted from England to the eastern half of the United States (including Iowa), rights to use water were incident to the ownership of land contiguous to the watercourse. The essence of the riparian theory is that each riparian owner has a right, equal to every other riparian owner, to use the water as it flows by his land. His right is usufructuary, that is, a right to use the water, and does not create an ownership interest in any particular quantum of water.

The classic statement of the riparian right is that it is a right to have the water flow by his land "undiminished in quantity and unimpaired in quality."[2] Obviously strict enforcement of such a right would mean that no riparian owner could ever make a consumptive use of the water; thus the right has come to be modified by a reasonable use concept. A riparian owner may use the water for his purposes so long as his use does not unreasonably interfere with the use of another riparian owner.[3] The reasonableness of a use comes in issue only if actual damage is being caused to another riparian. Reasonable use is a question of fact for jury deliberation, so each case must be decided on its own peculiar merits.[4]

In a pollution context, then, the discharge of effluent into a watercourse is actionable only where pollution is causing harm to some other riparian. If the damage is proved and the pollution found to be unreasonable, the injured riparian may seek to recover damages for his injury, to enjoin the harmful practice, or he may pursue both remedies.[5] The action to enforce or protect riparian rights against a polluter is usually premised upon the pollution constituting a private nuisance. An injunction may be granted where it is shown that the damage from the pollution is likely to be a continuing thing unless the discharge of the harmful effluent is stopped.[6] In certain cases where enjoining the polluter is not a realistic remedy, an award for permanent damages may be given.[7] For example, where a municipality is polluting a river to the great damage of an individual lower riparian, it may not be feasible to enjoin the discharge of city sewage, so the court will award permanent damages to the injured party. This amounts to the city's condemning an easement to pollute.

The efficacy of restraining pollution through private enforcement of riparian rights is considerably eroded by the several potent defenses that may be raised to such actions. In many cases actions have failed because they were not brought in time and the suit was barred by the statute of limitation, or a prescriptive right was found to exist. However, the greatest obstacle in most damage actions is proving that the injury is the result of the defendant's pollution. Typically, a stream is receiving effluents from more than one source, no one of which by itself would cause the alleged damage. Where the polluted state of a stream results from the cumulative effect of the discharge of varied effluents from several different points, it is nearly impossible to prove that a particular polluter is responsible for the damage.[8] Even where all polluters are joined as defendants, proving how the damage should be apportioned raises the same problems.[9] A few states hold concurrent polluters jointly and severally liable for the damage and assign the burden of apportionment to the defendants.[10] Several other states reach this result where it can be shown that the individual polluters knew or should have known that the cumulative effect of their separate acts of pollution would be to cause damage to those in the position of the plaintiff.[11]

Another sort of private control of pollution that may give rise to legal sanctions is that created by contract among riparian owners. Riparian owners may agree to allow the pollution of a watercourse beyond the normal limits. If the result of such an agreement is to create a pollution situation that only amounts to a private nuisance, the agreement is generally enforceable among the parties.[12] Similarly, an agreement calling for a standard of water quality higher than the normal would also be enforceable.

In summary it can be said with little danger of overstatement that the private remedies available to individuals damaged as the result of polluted water have never proved to be effective restraints for the control of water pollution. The greatest difficulty for the individual suitor has been the marshalling of the necessary facts to prove his case to a court which understandably lacks expertise in the biochemical phenomena associated with the problem. It should be understood, however, that these individual remedies have not disappeared with the advent of increased public controls and they are still available today for the aggrieved party who is not satisfied with the results obtained by the public control agency.

PUBLIC CONTROLS

The first public controls of water pollution were the rights conferred upon county attorneys to bring an action on behalf of the local citizenry to abate a public nuisance.[13] The rights available to individuals to agree to or defend against actions to abate pollution have ever been limited by the public's right to enjoin the creation or maintenance of a situation of water pollution deleterious to the public health and welfare. When pollution reaches this proportion, the public may intervene through its duly appointed representative and compel abatement. Historically, the difficulty with this type of control has been the extreme difficulty experienced by the few people most directly affected by the pollution in energizing the appropriate public officials.

Traditionally and currently, the principle repository of public control over water pollution has been the state government. From time to time the states have found it expedient to delegate or assign certain of their control prerogatives to other political entities. Certain types of regulations have been thought to be best handled at the local level by municipal corporations or county government units. Other pollution problems which overflow state boundaries in their causes and effects have been found to be most effectively dealt with by control organizations with multistate jurisdiction. Thus we find a movement toward interstate compacts that combine the information collection and enforcement capabilities of several states concerned with a common river basin. And finally, because it is believed by many that the problems of water pollution control have outstripped the ability of the states to deal with them effectively and have become a matter of national concern to be handled from Washington, it might be said that the states have defaulted to the federal government in certain of their control functions.

STATE REGULATION

In matters of regulation a state ordinarily acts through legislation that specifies the activity to be regulated, sets out the standard of conduct to be required, and charges some state agency with the administration of the regulatory scheme. The states' power to control water pollution is firmly established. The Supreme Court has laid down the general principal that any law reasonably designed to protect the health of a community is a constitutional exercise by the state of its police power.[14] Water pollution legislation designed to preserve and protect the public health and comfort, therefore, falls directly within the police power of the state. Its tendency to promote the public health and welfare cannot seriously be questioned.[15]

It also appears that the state legislature has absolute discretion to determine what constitutes a menace to health and could, if it chose, forbid discharges of any kind.[16] The legislative judgment as to what is harmful to public health is not subject to judicial review. If it appears from the statute itself that its real intent and purpose is the conservation and preservation of public health, then a court will only inquire whether such legislation is "beyond all question a plain, palpable invasion of rights secured by fundamental law."[17]

All states have legislation regulating water pollution and in every case the direct control responsibility is assigned to some state administrative agency.[18] A legislative delegation of authority over water pollution to an administrative agency is occasionally attacked as an unconstitutional delegation of the legislative power if the agency's discretion is not relatively restricted. For example, the New York Water Pollution Control Board submitted a pollution abatement plan to the city of Utica based on water quality standards developed by the board. The city resisted on the grounds that the New York pollution control law was unconstitutional as an invalid delegation of legislative authority to the board. The New York Court of Appeals rejected the city's argument and upheld the board's establishment of standards, saying that "the legislature is not required to break its plan down into fine detail in order to carry through its purpose of safeguarding the waters of the state."[19]

Similar results should be reached under almost all state statutes delegating administrative responsibilities to pollution control boards. The legislature may constitutionally confer discretion upon an administrative agency if it limits the field in which that discretion is to operate and provides standards to govern its exercise. It is enough if the legislature lays down an intelligible principle, specifying the standards or guides in as detailed a fashion as is reasonably practicable in the light of the complexities of the particular area to be regulated.[20]

The success of a state's control over the quality of its waters is heavily dependent upon the comprehensiveness of its pollution legislation and the character and efficiency of the regulatory agency administering the control program. One symptom of the growing concern about the pollution problem is the numerous revisions and reorganizations of the state pollution control machinery that have taken place since 1950. Originally, water pollution control was the exclusive domain of the state health departments. In more recent years many states have elected to relocate the responsibility for pollution control outside the health department or have reorganized the pollution control program within the health department. By 1965 sixteen states retained sole responsibility within the health department, twelve had created statutory agencies within the health department, twenty-one had created independent pollution control agencies, and one had placed the authority in its Fish and Game Commission.[21]

Where the decision was made to relocate the responsibility, the grounds for such a change were usually threefold: (1) that the public health aspects of the problem are no longer the matter of primary concern, (2) that the health department has too many other important responsibilities to devote to the pollution problem the energy it deserves, (3) that more funds may be marshalled for pollution control if the asking is not endorsed within a departmental budget.[22] Among those states that have left the control responsibility within the health department but have reorganized that department internally to achieve the desired regulatory mechanism, in most cases this reorganization has taken the form of a special board or commission created within the department and charged with the responsibility of carrying out the control program.[23] Generally, membership on this board is deliberately structured so that it reflects the various interests chiefly concerned with the problem.

Although the Council of State Governments has endorsed a Suggested Water Pollution Control Act,[24] there is by no means uniformity among the state regulatory statutes. Of course, lack of uniformity is not a criticism of state regulation because each state's law should be tailored to its particular control problems. Most acts, however, have a great deal in common and many of the recent revisions reflect the influence of the suggested act. The Water Pollution Control Act adopted by Iowa in 1965 is relatively typical of modern state statutes, so a survey of its provisions should furnish some insight into the general pattern of state legislative regulation of water pollution. The 1965 act opens by declaring it to be the policy of the state to "protect, maintain and improve the quality" of the waters of the state "for the propagation of wildlife, fish and aquatic life, and for domestic, agricultural, industrial, recreational and other legitimate (beneficial) uses."[25] Not all state statutes have such a declaration of policy, but on the whole it probably serves a worthwhile purpose in articulating the nature of the legislative concern which underlies the statute.

The next noteworthy portion of the Iowa act is the definition section in which ten terms of particular significance in the statute are explained. Of greatest interest among the ten terms is the definition assigned to "pollution."

"Pollution" means the contamination of any waters of the state so as to create a nuisance or render such waters unclean, noxious or impure so as to be actually harmful, detrimental or injurious to public health, safety or welfare, to domestic, commercial, industrial, agricultural or recreational use or to livestock, wild animals, birds, fish or other aquatic life.[26]

This definition differs somewhat from that used under the previous Iowa law, but the difference is one more of form than of substance.[27] The definition bears a strong resemblance to that included in the Suggested State Act and is quite similar to the definition employed by most other states.[28]

The next portion of the law creates the Iowa Water Pollution

Control Commission. The nine-man membership of the commission includes the Commissioner of Public Health; the director of the State Conservation Commission; the director of the Natural Resources Council; a qualified member of the staff of one of the state universities; the Secretary of Agriculture; and four public members, one of whom represents industry, one of whom represents municipal government, one an owner-operator farmer, and one to represent the public at large.[29] This deliberate effort to include on the control commission members representing all the major interest groups affected by pollution control is not unusual among the state acts, but it is by no means a universal practice. A number of states have chosen to limit the control board to public officials on the theory that including representatives from the groups subject to or interested in the regulation will inevitably cause conflicts that may handicap the board in carrying out its duties.[30] Little evidence exists to support the superiority of one type of board over the other.

Under the Iowa act, commission members not holding public office are appointed by the governor to staggered six-year terms without regard to political affiliation.[31] The provisions relating to the organization of the commission and its meetings are in no way unusual.[32] The integrity of the commission actions is promoted by a requirement that no commision member may have a direct financial interest in the work of the commission, nor may a member participate in a decision in which he has some personal interest.[33]

The next portion of the statute prescribing the powers and duties of the commission is perhaps the most significant part of the act. The commission is empowered and directed (1) to generally administer and enforce the water pollution laws, (2) to develop comprehensive plans and programs to deal with pollution,(3) to cause the investigations of alleged pollution situations, (4) to adopt and change water quality standards for any waters of the state as it deems necessary, (5) to review and approve or disapprove plans for disposal systems and through the Department of Health to control the issuance, modification and revocation of permits for the installation and operation of disposal systems, (6) to make rules and regulations necessary for the conduct of the commission and the carrying out of its responsibilities, (7) to cooperate with other state or interstate pollution control agencies in establishing quality standards for interstate waters, (8) to hold, *in banc* or individually, hearings necessary to discharge its duties.[34]

Several of these powers and duties deserve further comment, but first it should be observed that to comprehend fully the commission's responsibilities, it is necessary to understand the relationship between the commission and the Department of Health. The commission is created as an independent agency within the Department of Health. The commission is primarily a policy-making body. It must depend on the health department to conduct its investigations and enforce its orders as it has no separate staff. To this end the commission is given the power to direct the Department of Health to do its bidding in matters where some form of action is required.[35] This relationship is a likely one that is easier to work out in practice than it is to depict on an organization chart. For example, a health department officer currently serves as technical secretary to the commission and undoubtedly facilitates the coordination between the commission and the department.[36]

The procedures by which the Iowa commission operates to supervise and enforce water pollution control are representative of the operations of most state pollution control agencies. Investigations may be called for by the commission on its own decision or the commission may be compelled to order an investigation through the written petition of five different types of petitioners.[37] Regardless of how the commission determines the situations it wants surveyed, the Division of Public Health Engineering of the health department actually conducts the investigation.[38] When an investigation is made, it must be full and complete.

If the investigation shows pollution to exist, the commission gives notice of its findings to the person, persons, or industry alleged to be responsible for the pollution. Then follows a fourteen-day negotiation period during which the commission and its staff are prohibited from making public the allegation of pollution.[39] The purpose of this moratorium on public statements is to facilitate an informal settlement of the particular pollution problem. The hope in each case is that the commission and the alleged polluter can arrive at an abatement plan and time schedule satisfactory to both parties and thereby avoid further proceedings. If such a plan is agreed upon, the commission issues orders formally restating and approving the plan. The negotiation procedure specified in the Iowa act is a unique legislative provision among water pollution control acts, but the informal procedure it encourages is a practice administratively adopted by several states.

If the negotiation procedure fails to bring about the desired changes, a hearing is scheduled on the matter. The hearing procedure is prescribed in detail and is well designed to protect both the public interest and the rights of the alleged polluter.[40] If as the result of the hearing it is determined that some action is necessary to correct the situation, the commission may simply order the polluter to desist from the practice found to result in pollution or it may order a change in the method of discharging effluent.[41]

The order of the commission is appealable within   thirty days to the district court of the county in which the alleged offense was committed or the final order was entered.[42] The appeal procedure is fully spelled out, and the only point worthy of particular note is that the appeal will be tried *de novo* as a suit in equity.[43] Many states treat the orders of the control commissions in the same manner as lower court decisions and review them only for errors of law or substantial abuse of discretion.[44]

Should the polluter fail to obey the orders of the commission, such fact may be certified by the commission to the local district court, which may then order compliance with the order on penalty of contempt. A maximum fine of $100 may be assessed for each offense of contempt. The commission may also enforce its orders by requesting the Attorney General to institute an action to enjoin the unlawful practice.[45]

Some states provide not only for injunctive relief preventing discharge of wastes and criminal penalties for failure to abide by commission orders but also provide that the board may issue a positive order that the offender make acquisition of or construct facilities necessary for the treatment of the waste.[46] Minnesota's act goes further than most in that it authorizes the control commissioner to assume the power of the administrative officers of the municipality relating to construction, installation, or operation of the disposal system if the officers fail to comply with an order of the commission.[47] The Minnesota act also gives its commission the power to determine if cooperation between two or more municipalities is necessary and if it determines such cooperation to be desirable, it can order the municipalities to execute a contract to that effect. If such a contract is not arranged, the commissioner can assume and formulate a contract in accordance with the commission's order.[48]

In the course of determining, under a procedure similar to that outlined earlier, whether or not a particular discharge results in pollution, a pollution control commission must evaluate the practice at issue by some sort of water quality criteria. Most state acts authorize the control commission to establish standards for effluents or for receiving waters and to classify the state's waters with respect to such standards and the uses for which the waters may be suitable.[49] The model act suggests that the establishment of standards be discretionary with the control commission and most states have followed this suggestion.[50] The Iowa commission is expressly authorized to formulate water quality standards.[51] Although the commission is expressly directed to give consideration to no less than fourteen different factors if they establish standards,[52] the decision whether to pronounce standards is clearly discretionary with the commission.[53]

Ideally, the first order of business of a new control commission would be the formulation of water quality standards for the waters of the state. These standards would then be available for application to all cases coming before the commission for hearing. Unfortunately, in the real world the formulation of statewide standards is an extremely complex and time-consuming enterprise and the day-to-day cases press relentlessly for decision. Therefore, most control commissions develop their quality standards piecemeal as cases requiring the applications of such quality criteria come on for hearing.[54] The Iowa commission is currently operating in this fashion. It is not a procedure about which one can be very critical so long as the quality standards developed are applied fairly to similar cases, and the ultimate need to develop standards for waters of the state not yet involved in a case before the commission is recognized.

In two states, New Hampshire and Maine, the legislature established four classes of receiving waters and standards for them, and then the legislature classified every major body of surface water.[55] There is a provision for changing the classification of a body of water upon recommendation of the control board to the state legislature. In Vermont the legislature established the identical rigid standards as established in Maine and New Hampshire but delegated to the control board the responsibility of classifying the waters according to these standards.[56]

New York is an example of a state where the control commission has exercised its power both to adopt standards and to classify the waters. There the act provides that there are variable factors and no single standard of quality and purity is applicable to all waters and directs consideration of best usage in the interest of the public with regard to established criteria.[57] Acting under the authority of this provision, the New York Water Pollution Control Board has adopted classifications and standards of quality and purity.[58]

Another distinct power of the control commission that greatly facilitates its supervision over water pollution in the state is that which concerns the requirement of a permit to construct or alter a disposal system.[59] The permit requirement gives the control commission a powerful leverage on municipalities and industries to force the construction of adequate disposal facilities. Although in Iowa the permit technically issues from the Department of Health, under the new act the commission must approve the plans and specifications before the permit may be granted.[60] Carrying on of the specified activities without a permit is made punishable by $1,000 fine.[61] Permits granted under this provision are subject to modification and revocation by the commission.[62] No express provision for a hearing on the modification or revocation is contained within the act, but presumably the commission would grant such a hearing under its general administrative powers.[63]

It has been claimed from time to time that the issuance of revocable disposal system permits retards the growth of industry and indirectly prevents greater pollution control because a plant is hesitant to build any larger system than it absolutely has to for fear that its permit will be revoked or modified and its investment thereby squandered. This argument seems unrealistic in view of the wide-scale use of revocable permits among the states and the small likelihood that a change in the terms of the permit would cause little more than an adjustment in the way a disposal system is employed.

Two other somewhat related powers of the commission deserve mention. The commission is authorized to develop comprehensive plans and programs for pollution control[64] and to cooperate with other state and interstate control agencies in establishing objectives for interstate waters.[65] These powers tie together in some respects and it is hoped that the Iowa commission will attempt to use them in concert to institute sound and forward-looking programs. The one criticism that is constantly, and all too often fairly, leveled at state pollution control agencies is that they are basically a hand-to-mouth operation giving little thought to the development of comprehensive programs that take into account likely future needs. The increased urbanization and industrialization that certainly lie in Iowa's future make inescapable the need for progressive planning in the state and in the region.

Encouraging the development of local responsibility for pollution control is an example of the kind of program that the commission might consider looking to for the future. The Iowa act does not authorize the creation of special local agencies for pollution control as do the statutes of several other states.[66] Perhaps this omission is currently justified by Iowa's relative lack of concentration of either population or industrial activity. The day may arrive, however, when pollution in certain areas of the state may be more effectively policed by local sanitary districts than by a state commission.[67]

One area where many state control acts are weak is in what might be called enabling provisions. Several states that have recently revised their pollution control laws included in their new legislation provisions to assist potential polluters in the construction of adequate disposal facilities.[68] Experience has shown that rigorous enforcement of pollution control laws is not enough to prevent pollution in certain instances. As the Suggested State Act points out, where the control commission issues an order for improvement of a disposal facility, the order may achieve the desired result only if the requisite financial ability or other corrective capacity is possessed by the offender.[69]

For example, a cease and desist order does little good against a municipality that has reached its limit of bonded indebtedness or whose voters will not approve a bond issue to construct a new sewage treatment plant. The same sort of problem may also arise in connection with an industry whose capital structure is not adequate to finance the type of disposal system required by the control laws.

Iowa municipalities may face both obstacles if the correction of a pollution situation is approached through issuance of general obligation bonds for the construction of an expensive disposal system. The Iowa constitution limits the bonded indebtedness of a municipality to 5 per cent of the assessed value of the property within the municipality.[70] By statute a city's indebtedness is further limited to 1.25 per cent of the actual value of the property within the city.[71] Further, approval of a general obligation bond issue to build a disposal system requires a majority vote of the local citizens.[72]

Fortunately, Iowa municipalities have available to them a financing alternative that is not subject to the aforementioned limits on indebtedness and that does not require voter approval. The provisions of the Iowa code authorizing the issuance of revenue bonds to finance municipal sewer facilities have long been used to pay for waste disposal plant construction.[73] In point of fact this practice is almost universal in Iowa today.

INTERSTATE CONTROLS

The concept of pollution control authorities with jurisdiction to regulate a river basin, without regard to the fact that the area regulated crosses state lines, has great appeal from the standpoint of administrative efficiency. Such an agency can establish reasonable water quality standards and enforce them with a degree of consistency not achievable by the separate states involved. Because its authority extends the entire length of the river, the orders of such a regional agency are likely to be met with greater acceptance because the regulated offender can be confident that other parties in a similar position are subject to the same regulation, a circumstance that does not always exist where control agencies from different states may be involved.

Such interstate pollution control agencies have been created in a number of regions to deal with pollution problems that overlap state boundaries.[74] Several of these regional authorities derive their jurisdiction from interstate compacts entered into by the states involved and approved by Congress.[75] The creation of a formal interstate compact is a rather cumbersome process and the difficulty involved in organizing in this fashion has no doubt discouraged some states from pursuing this format. For the interstate agency to possess truly enforceable regulatory powers, an interstate compact is required, for short of such an arrangement any state could deny the obligation imposed by the agreement and the other states would be powerless to compel performance.

This is not to say, however, that agreements less formalized than the traditional interstate compact would not be adequate to handle the task of regional control. In fact, today, a number of informal regional agreements among states sharing a common watershed are assisting in the development of uniform quality standards and objectives within the affected region.[76]

The handling of water pollution control on a natural regional basis rather than adhering to artificial state boundaries in the organization of the control agencies is clearly an alternative that will receive increased consideration in the future. The Suggested State Act empowers local control agencies to cooperate in such regional projects and the federal Water Pollution Control Act certainly encourages developments in this direction.[77]

FEDERAL REGULATION

The entry of the federal government into water pollution control was first clearly made in the federal Water Pollution Control Act of 1948.[78] Since that time the interest of the federal government has been gradually expanded through amendments in 1956,[79] 1961,[80] and 1965.[81] The amendment passed October 2, 1965, establishes a Federal Water Pollution Control Administration as a separate agency in the Department of Health, Education, and Welfare. (In early 1966 the President moved the Federal Water Pollution Control Administration from HEW to the Department of the Interior.) This newly created authority is directed to supervise the activity of the department in the water pollution area and takes over the responsibilities formerly exercised by various agencies within the department, most notably the work of the Public Health Service under the direction of the Surgeon General.

Generally the federal government enters the water pollution control field on several levels: (1) support for research to discover new and better methods of waste disposal, (2) technical services and counsel to the state, (3) grants to the state, (4) construction grants to help finance new municipal disposal facilities, and (5) enforcement of pollution controls on interstate or navigable waters. Because this chapter is primarily concerned with regulation of water pollution, the research, grant, and technical assistance aspects of the federal program will be passed by with the observation that to

1965 they have probably had a more significant impact on the pollution situation than the enforcement powers that we will examine in detail.

In the first place it should be noted that the Federal Water Pollution Control Act expressly states, "It is hereby declared to be the policy of Congress to recognize, preserve, and protect the primary responsibilities and rights of the States in preventing and controlling water pollution."[82] This guiding policy should be kept in mind while the enforcement powers of the federal control administration are reviewed.

As noted above, the enforcement jurisdiction of the federal control administration is limited to interstate and navigable waters. This limitation is more illusory than it might appear at first blush owing to the fact that the administration is authorized to deal with pollution occurring on tributaries of interstate streams as well as that found on the interstate stream itself[83] and because of the broad definition placed on navigable waters. Interstate waters are those forming a part of or flowing across the boundaries of two or more states. As the administration views the test of navigability, a stream is navigable if it is navigable in fact or has once been navigable or by the reasonable expenditures of funds can be made navigable.[84]

The jurisdiction of the federal control administration to abate pollution can be invoked in several ways. In regard to interstate pollution the administration must act whenever a request is received from a governor or the water pollution control agency of a state in which the health or welfare of its citizens are being endangered by pollution discharged into the interstate waters by another state. The administration may also act on its own initiative in a case of interstate pollution as described above if on the basis of reports, surveys, or studies there is reason to believe that such a situation exists. Action by the administration is discretionary in the latter instance.[85]

Where the pollution complained of is wholly intrastate, the administration may enter the enforcement picture only on the invitation of the governor, and the exercise of federal authority is discretionary and may be withheld if it is found that the effect of the pollution on legitimate water uses is not of sufficient significance.[86]

The procedure under which federal enforcement action is conducted is detailed in the federal act. There are three procedural stages, each step following the previous one in orderly sequence when it fails to obtain the action required to resolve the problem. First, there is a conference. The state and federal parties meet together to evaluate the pollution situation, determine what delays are being encountered, and agree as to what remedial steps are required. One or, if necessary, a number of sessions of the conference may be held.

When agreement upon necessary remedial action is reached, the states are given a reasonable time and opportunity to correct the problem and are encouraged to exercise the state authority.[87]

If, after the conference, the remedial steps are not forthcoming, a public hearing is called. A hearing board of five or more members is appointed including representatives of the states involved, the Department of the Interior and other federal agencies that may have an interest. Sworn testimony is received by the board, which makes findings and recommendations upon the evidence that is presented to it. The secretary sends the board's findings and recommendations to the specific polluters, together with the notice specifying a reasonable time for abatement of the pollution.[88]

If the board's recommendations and the Secretary of the Interior's notice do not obtain compliance, court action is then instituted. The secretary may request the Attorney General to bring a suit on behalf of the United States in interstate pollution cases. In an intrastate situation he may do so only with the written consent of the governor of that state.[89]

The 1965 amendments to the federal act spell out a new procedure for establishing water quality standards for interstate waters. Under the new provision the governor of a state, or the state pollution control agency, may within one year after the date of enactment file a letter of intent that the state will establish before June 30, 1967, quality standards applicable to interstate waters and adopt a plan for enforcement of such standards. If the standards and plans are adopted in accordance with the letter of intent and the Secretary of the Interior determines that the plans are consistent with the criteria established by the act, the state standards shall be the standards applied by the federal administration to interstate waters in or bordering that state.[90]

If the state does not adopt its own standards in the allotted time, or the standards adopted do not satisfy the Secretary of the Interior, or a revision of properly established standards is desired by the governor of the state or the secretary, the secretary, after reasonable notice and consultation with appropriate state and federal agencies, may prepare regulations setting forth the water quality standards for the interstate waters of the state involved. If the state does not adopt satisfactory quality standards within six months after the secretary has published his regulation, the secretary may promulgate his standards for the interstate waters of the state.[91] The governor of any state affected by standards promulgated under the above procedure may within thirty days request a hearing before a special hearing board which has primary power over the challenged regulations.[92] The hearing board is structured in such a way that a majority of its members will be persons who are not federal employees.[93]

Once the standards are finally established, the federal administration may enforce them against violators through the abatement procedure outlined earlier. It is specifically provided, however, that violators must receive 180 days notice of their alleged violation of the quality standards before any abatement action is initiated.[94]

In final analysis it would appear that the recent amendments to the federal act reveal in bold relief the basic dilemma confronting the federal government in the area of water pollution control. Congress wants to make a frontal assault on what it regards as a serious national problem, yet it is reluctant to make too great an incursion into the responsibilities traditionally assigned to the states. The result is a program that combines the carrot and the stick, both of which have grown appreciably in size since the entry of the federal government into the fray seventeen years ago. Although there have been some difficulties, the record seems to show that this "push and pull" approach has been generally successful, both from the standpoint of avoiding conflicts with the states and, more important, making substantial inroads into the continually expanding pollution problem.[95]

CONCLUSION

From the legal standpoint water quality control is a problem most difficult of solution because it requires the striking of a delicate balance between varied conflicting interests, all having substantial social weight and all being urged with great fervor. Part of the difficulty stems from the fact that legal institutions capable of weighing efficiently such diverse and discrete interests have evolved only recently. Even more to the point, as developed in preceding chapters, reliable information concerning the physical, economic, and social factors involved has not always been extant and may not be available in the degree of refinement necessary for the sophisticated evaluation required.

This chapter has highlighted briefly the regulatory structure affecting water quality on different levels ranging from private suits based on nuisance to the federal Water Pollution Control Administration. One uninitiated to the complexities of the pollution problem might be tempted to ask, "With all this regulation, why de we have so much pollution?" One answer is that although great strides have been made in pollution control, regulation has simply not been able to catch up with the problem. An even better answer is that regulation alone is not enough. Effective handling of a problem of the magnitude of water pollution requires an enormous investment of effort and money on the part of our society. If the public could be made aware of the problem and some understanding of what is required for alleviation could be generated, there is reason to be optimistic that the necessary resolve and wherewithal might be forthcoming. Stimulating such an awareness and sparking such an understanding is the major purpose of the conference on which this book is based.

NOTES

1. Cited in Berman, *The Nature and Functions of Law*, 9 (1958).
2. Pomery, *Riparian Rights*, § 8 (1887). The law of the western states is governed by the "appropriation doctrine." It will not be discussed in this paper. For a thorough discussion see Weil, *Water Rights in the Western States* (3rd ed. 1911).
3. See Lauer, "The Riparian Right as Property," in *Water Resources and the Law*, 169 (1948).
4. See Restatement, Torts. § 853 (1939).
5. See Note, 50 *Iowa L. Rev.*, 141 (1964).
6. See Kenyon, "What Can a Riparian Proprietor Do?" 21 *Minn. L. Rev.* 512 (1937).
7. *Platt Bros. & Co. v. City of Waterbury*, 72 Conn. 531, 551, 45 Atl. 154, 162 (1900); *Farmers Irrigation Co. v. Game & Fish Comm'n*, 149 Colo. 318, 369 P. 2d 557 (1962); *Smallpage v. Turlock Irrigation Dist.*, 26 Cal. App. 2d 538, 545, 79 P. 2d 752, 755 (3d Dist. 1938).
8. See Wigmore, "Joint Tortfeasors and Severance of Damages; Making the Innocent Party Suffer Without Redress," 17 *Ill. L. Rev.*, 458 (1923).
9. See Prosser, "Joint Torts and Several Liability," 25 *Calif. L. Rev.*, 413 (1937).
10. Kansas, Louisiana, Maryland and Oklahoma apparently reach this result. See Note, 50 *Iowa L. Rev.*, 141, 148 (1964).
11. *McKinney v. Deneen*, 231 N.C. 540, 58 S.E. 2d 108 (1950); *Bowman v. Humphrey*, 124 Iowa 744, 747, 100 N.W. 854, 855 (1904) (dictum).
12. *Wright v. Best*, 19 Cal. 2d 368, 121 P. 2d 702 (1942); *Johnson v. Armour & Co.*, 69 N.D. 769, 291 N.W. 113 (1910).
13. See Note, 24 *Geo. Wash. L. Rev.* 302, 307 n. 32 (1956).
14. See *Hutchingson v. City of Valdosta*, 227 U.S. 303 (1913); "Statutory Treatment of Industrial Stream Pollution," 24 *Geo. Wash. L. Rev.*, 302, 313 (1955).
15. *City of Niles v. Stream Control Comm.*, 296 Mich. 650, 654, 296 N.W. 713 (1941); *Shirley v. New Hampshire Water Pollution Comm.*, 100 N.H. 294, 299, 300, 124 A. 2d 189 (1956); *State Board of Health v. City of Greenville*, 86 Ohio St. 1, 21–22, 98 N.E. 1019, 1021 (1912); *Board of Purification of Waters v. Town of Bristol*, 51 R.I. 243, 153 Atl. 879 (1913).
16. *New Jersey v. Chemical Co. of Am.*, 90 N.J. Eq. 425, 107 Atl. 164 (1919).
17. *State Bd. of Health v. City of Greenville*, 86 Ohio St. 1, 21–22, 98 N.E. 1019, 1021 (1921).
18. See Stein, "Problems and Programs in Water Pollution," 2 *Nat. Res. J.*, 388, 407 (1962).
19. *City of Utica v. Water Pollution Control Bd.*, 5 N.Y. 2d 164, 156 N.E. 2d 301, 304 (1959).
20. *City of Utica v. Water Pollution Control Bd.*, 5 N.Y. 2d 164, 156 N.E. 2d 304, (1959).
21. The present distribution of authority for water pollution control activities among the 50 state governments are as follows:
   (1) Sixteen states retain water pollution control responsibility in their state health agencies. These are as follows:

Alaska	Georgia	Kansas
Arizona	Hawaii	Maryland
Florida	Idaho	Massachusetts

Nevada	New York	Rhode Island
New Jersey	Oklahoma	Wyoming
New Mexico		

(2) Twenty-one states have placed their water pollution control responsibility in independent water agencies. These are as follows:

Alabama	Michigan	Tennessee
California	Minnesota	Texas
Connecticut	Montana	Vermont
Delaware	New Hampshire	Virginia
Illinois	North Carolina	Washington
Louisiana	North Dakota	West Virginia
Maine	South Dakota	Wisconsin

(3) The twelve other states have created statutory agencies within their state health agencies. These are as follows:

Arkansas	Kentucky	Oregon
Colorado	Missouri	Pennsylvania
Indiana	Nebraska	South Carolina
Iowa	Ohio	Utah

(4) Mississippi places the authority in its Fish and Game Commission.

22. See Wilson, "Legal Aspects of Water Pollution Control," in *Proceedings; The National Conference on Water Pollution*, 361 (1961).
23. See *Hearings Before a Special Subcommittee on Air and Water Pollution of the Senate Committee on Public Works*, 87 (88th Cong., 1st Sess., 1963). (Hereinafter cited as *Hearings*).
24. *Suggested State Water Pollution Control Act*, Public Health Serv. Publ. No. 49 (1950). Approximately 40 states have relied on this model act to some extent in the revision of their pollution control laws.
25. Acts of the 61st General Assembly, Ch. 375, § 1 (Iowa 1965). (Hereinafter cited as Iowa Act).
26. Iowa Act, § 2(4).
27. See Iowa Code, § 135.18 (1962).
28. Compare Minn. Stat. Ann., § 115.01 (1945).
29. Iowa Act, § 4.
30. See Wilson, *supra* note 22 at 361.
31. Iowa Act, § 5.
32. See Iowa Act, §§ 6–8.
33. Iowa Act, § 7.
34. Iowa Act, § 9. The act enumerates ten numbered powers, but numbers 5–7 all deal with the issuance of permits so they have been combined in the listing above.
35. *E.g.*, Iowa Act, §§ 9(6), 11.
36. R. J. Schliekelman of the Iowa Department of Health currently serves as technical secretary to the commission.
37. Iowa Act, § 9(3).
38. Iowa Act, § 10.
39. Iowa Act, § 12.
40. See Iowa Act, §§ 12, 15–17.
41. Iowa Act, § 17(3).
42. Iowa Act, § 18.
43. See Iowa Act, §§ 18–22.
44. See, *e.g.*, Code of Va., § 62–37 (1950).
45. Iowa Act, §§ 23 & 24.
46. See, *e.g.*, Ill. Ann. Stat. Ch. 19, § 145.6(c)(2) (1963); Ky. Rev. Stat., § 220.610(8) (1959); N.Y. Public Health Laws, § 1210.3(b) (1959).
47. Minn. Stat. Ann., § 115.48 (1963). Such powers shall include, without limitation, the power to levy taxes and assessments, to prescribe service charges, to borrow money, to issue bonds, to employ assistance, to let contracts, and all acts necessary to effectuate the purposes of the order.
48. Minn. Stat. Ann., § 115.49(2) (1963). Statistical analysis indicates that

per capita sewage treatment plant costs are lowest in the one-million-and-over population bracket. Here the cost runs $12.54 per capita and in cities of 100,000 the per capita average in initial plant costs is $22.53 and $45.95 for communities of 6,000 population. McCallum, "Formula for Economy: Combined Federal-City-Industry Action," *Waste Engineering* (Oct. 1961).

49. See, *e.g.*, N.Y. Public Health Laws, 1205 (1959); Ill. Ann. Stat., Ch. 19, 145.2 (1963).
50. See Wilson, *supra* note 22 at 364–68.
51. Iowa Act, § 9(4).
52. Iowa Act, § 13.
53. The language of § 9(4) states the board's power to establish standards in terms of "as it shall deem necessary for the purposes of the Act."
54. See Wilson, *supra* note 22 at 364–69.
55. N.H. Rev. Stat. Ann., § 149.3, .6 (1964); Rev. Stat. Me. Ch. 79, §§ 2, 3, 15 (Cum. Supp. 1963). Both the New Hampshire and the Maine acts set up standards for four different classes (A, B_1 & B_2, C, and D). Class A waters are defined as being good enough for bathing and public water supplies. The dissolved oxygen content of such waters shall not be less than 75 per cent saturation and contain not more than 100 coliform bacteria per 100 milliliters of water. There shall be no discharge of sewage or other waste into water of this classification and no deposits of such material on the banks of such waters in such a manner that transfer of the material into the water is likely. The acts define each class in a similar manner through Class D which is used primarily for the transportation of sewage and industrial waste. The listing of all the classified waters in the Rev. Stat. Me., Ch. 79, § 15 required 36 pages.
56. Ver. Stat. Ann. Tit. 10, §§ 904–8 (1958).
57. N.Y. Public Health Laws, § 1205 (1959).
58. See 10A § 10B N.Y.C.R.R. §§ 100–58.
59. See Wilson, *supra* note 22 at 370, 371.
60. Iowa Act, §§ 9(5)–(7), 25.
61. Iowa Act, § 25(2).
62. Iowa Act, § 9(6).
63. See Iowa Act, § 9(10).
64. Iowa Act, § 9(2).
65. Iowa Act, § 9(9).
66. See, *e.g.*, Minn. Stat. Ann., § 115.46 (1963).
67. See, *e.g.*, Ohio's handling of the Cleveland pollution problem through a metropolitan sanitary district authorized by Ohio Rev. Code, Ch. 6111.29 (1954).
68. See, *e.g.*, Ind. Stat. Ann., § 68.528 (1961).
69. Suggested State Water Pollution Control Act, Explanatory Statement, 2 (1951).
70. Iowa Constitution, Art. 11, § 3.
71. Iowa Code, § 407.1(1962).
72. Iowa Code, § 407.10(1962).
73. Such Bonds are issued in accordance with Ch. 23 of the Iowa Code under authorization found in § 391.12 & .93. The revenue upon which the bonds are based is essentially the revenue realized under the sewer tax authorized by § 391.13.
74. See Note, 24 *Geo. Wash. L. Rev.*, 302 (1956).
75. See *e.g.*, Potomac River Compact, 54 Stat. 748 (1940); Ohio R. Valley Sanitation Compact, 54 Stat. 752 (1940).
76. See Cleary, "The Needs and Obligations of Interstate Agencies," in *Proc., National Conference on Water Pollution,* 270 (1961).
77. See Suggested Act, § 4(b); Federal Water Pollution Control Act, 33 U.S.C. 466b (1963).
78. 62 Stat. 1155 (1948).
79. 70 Stat. 498 (1956).

80. 75 Stat. 210 (1961).
81. Water Quality Act of 1965, 79 Stat. 903 (1965).
82. 33 U.S.C.A. 466(a) (1963).
83. 33 U.S.C.A. 466g (1963).
84. See "Testimony of Murray Stein," *Hearings,* 50–51 (1963)
85. 33 U.S.C.A. 466g(c) (1963).
86. 33 U.S.C.A. 466g(c)(i) (1963).
87. 33 U.S.C.A. 466g(c) & (d) (1963).
88. 33 U.S.C.A. 466g(e) (1963).
89. 33 U.S.C.A. 466g(f) (1963).
90. Water Quality Act of 1965, 79 Stat. 903, § 5(a)(1).
91. Water Quality Act of 1965, 79 Stat. 903, § 5(a)(2).
92. Water Quality Act of 1965, 79 Stat. 903, § 5(a)(4).
93. *Ibid.*
94. Water Quality Act of 1965, 79 Stat. 903, § 5(a)(5).
95. See "Testimony of Murray Stein," *Hearings,* 47–88 (1963)

CHAPTER 5

WATER POLLUTION POLICIES AND POLITICS

FRED A. CLARENBACH

In 1945 Benjamin H. Hibbard, a famous alumnus of Iowa State College, was attempting to explain American farm policies to some Wisconsin graduate students at a meeting of the Taylor-Hibbard Club in Madison. A foreign student, not understanding the intricate business very well, asked Professor Hibbard to tell him in one sentence just what the American farmers wanted. The good professor paused a moment and then said, "Well, in one sentence: The farmer wants all he can get plus 10 per cent."

Twenty years later in the same city, at two different meetings concerned with policies for clean and dirty water, I was reminded of Hibbard's comment.

Opening a conference on water resources management, Governor Warren Knowles of Wisconsin said, "The color of this problem is green." And at that point he did not mean the algae on the lakes. Later in the same day Governor Nelson Rockefeller of New York stressed the view that money is the core of the problem of improving water quality. On a second occasion, Senator Gaylord Nelson forcefully stated his impression that a massive capital expenditure of $60–$100 billion, in large part federal funds, is needed to clean up the streams and lakes of the country.

These several observations suggest some core truths about the nature of the political struggle. Politics is a process for deciding who gets what, when, and how. Who is to get water of what quality, how much and when, and how is all this to be arranged through private

FRED A. CLARENBACH is professor of regional planning, University of Wisconsin, Madison, Wisconsin.

and public action? Who is to be restrained from putting how much of what kinds of wastes into which parts of the country's hydrologic systems? Who is to be permitted to use the waters for waste disposal, and under what terms and conditions? And the $60 billion question is: Who is to pay the unavoidably high costs which must be met if the quality of ground and surface waters is to be protected and significantly improved?

ALTERNATIVES FOR ACTION

The various answers and nonanswers to all these questions are obviously affected by different meanings of "clean water" and by differing perceptions of the alternatives for action. Though no one is willing to champion positively the cause of dirty water, one man's notion of clean water may in fact be another man's idea of pretty low-grade wet stuff. At another extreme are some people who seem to want all streams and lakes to be "absolutely clean," plus 10 per cent. A variant is the idea that the proper objective should be to make all surface waters fully potable. Extreme views of the latter kinds are seldom if ever associated with practical conceptions of technical or financial feasibility. This is not to deny their value as campaign weapons and slogans, but they do not contribute much to a sober understanding of the real issues.

Nevertheless, probably the greater obstacles to understanding and rational action are found at the first end of the spectrum, among some (not all) of the industrial and agricultural polluters. These groups usually want to hold on to whatever advantages and privileges they may have in using streams for waste disposal. Regulations perceived as adverse are typically resisted unless resistance seems futile. Ordinarily, in a period of mounting public pressure for water quality improvements industry groups plead for postponement of the effective dates of proposed regulatory measures to allow time for more research and possible technological breakthroughs. They often allege that existing regulations are working well and that there is no need for change. Almost uniformly they favor keeping governmental regulation at the local and state level. Federal regulation presumably would be not so mild, would be less susceptible to local private influence, and would be more effective on the whole. Very often the final industrial argument is that the costs of compliance would be impossibly high and would either seriously cripple the industry and inhibit expansion or force it out of business or into another state. Undoubtedly, some of these arguments are valid at some times and places. Very often, however, the evidence to support them is quite inadequate. But again, just as with the ideas and slogans of the clean water absolutists, the polluters' arguments may be potent propaganda weapons in the continuing political battle to protect their interests as they see them.

WATER USE AS PUBLIC POLICY

Back of all the noise and confusion lies the serious question: What combinations of water uses, local and regional, should be planned for and sought as a matter of public policy? This question cannot be answered sensibly without considering the different quality requirements for water in different uses and the costs of meeting the requirements, as well as the values or benefits of the various uses. Where conflicts of uses occur, a cost of providing quality suitable for use A may be the elimination of opportunity for use B; or the B use may be cut back to a point compatible with the A use at a certain level. Ideally, there would be a process of comparing benefits and costs at the margin, and there would be a series of trade-offs to achieve an optimum pattern of uses and net benefits. Unfortunately, neither the economist nor anyone else can tell the statesman and administrator just how to find the proper unit values for all the beneficial uses of water. As Braybrooke and Lindblom put it, the basic difficulties "arise from the fact that values must be coordinated without fixed coordinating principles."[1]

Today there is an especially important and growing conflict between the beneficial use of water for waste disposal and the complex of recreational, esthetic, and environmental amenity values of good quality water in the streams and lakes. These conflicts will probably never be resolved fully, but they will be dealt with in a long and overlapping series of disjointed incremental adjustments. This is the mode of action characteristic of a pluralist political system. I have no doubt that the result will be a substantial improvement in the quality of most of the surface waters in the country and the better maintenance of water quality generally. Given the currently developing public perceptions and judgments of the recreational-esthetic-environmental values of higher quality waters, these kinds of outcomes are almost certain.

The important and interesting questions now are those relating to the evolving roles of the states, the federal government, and regional agencies, and to the kinds of regulatory measures and financial incentives which may be used most effectively and equitably in this growing enterprise of water quality management.

STATE CONTROL

With few exceptions the states have been slow and weak in developing programs for water pollution control. Often the statutes provide inadequate powers for administrative agencies; sometimes the authority and responsibilities are scattered among too many state agencies; and usually, the funds appropriated are insufficient to support competent professional staffs of the size necessary to do a good job. Though Wisconsin is not typical, in that it has for many years maintained a program remarkably successful in most respects, it does exemplify some of the weaknesses of current state programs. The Wisconsin law does not authorize the setting of stream standards, and compliance with some of the antipollution orders of the Board of Health and the Committee on Water Pollution still has not been accomplished many years after issuance of the initial order. In addition to those two agencies, the Conservation Commission, the Public Service Commission, the Attorney General, and several others have roles of some importance in the pollution control enterprise. The relatively good coordination actually achieved in Wisconsin may depend too heavily on the luck of good informal relations among the staffs of the several independent agencies with closely related functions. Finally, the Wisconsin state appropriations and the permitted levels of professional salaries fall considerably short of the amounts required for doing the job of water pollution control as effectively as public opinion now seems ready to demand. Were it not for a substantial annual grant of federal funds for support of the activities of the state Committee on Water Pollution, the shortcomings of the program would be considerably greater.

An acquaintance with some of the recent reports and summaries of pollution control agencies and programs developing in many other states suggests that there are "certain patterns, similarities, trends, and styles" which are observable even in a gross view of the evolving situation.[2] First, water pollution controls based on the common law are still available and are used at times. Court action to abate a public nuisance may be instituted and is sometimes successful. Private persons injured by pollution may seek and sometimes collect damages through court action. But such piecemeal resort to the courts typically has been and still is costly and generally inadequate for dealing with water pollution broadly and effectively.

A second distinguishable phase in the development of public action in this field was that of giving state health departments statutory authority to abate nuisances, to protect domestic water supplies from contamination, and to adopt regulations to insure such protection. Often the state conservation commissions or fish and game departments were given similar powers for the protection of fish and wildlife. Sometimes additional agencies were significantly involved, and difficulties of achieving reasonably unified policies and coordinated action inevitably arose. As a consequence several states in recent years have set up a single administrative agency with broad primary authority for control and abatement of water pollution in the state. When such establishments are created, there may be provision "(a) for representation of the several interests concerned in water pollution, either on an advisory board or on the control board itself, (b) for the definition and determination of pollution, usually by stream standards or classifications, (c) for the enforcement of abatement orders, with penalties for non-compliance, and (d) for hearings and appeals of parties affected by actions of the agency."[3]

Usually a state has delegated to certain local officials or to units of local government either limited or fairly broad powers for pollution control. With few exceptions, however, the local governing bodies and locally elected officers (including judges) have not vigorously enforced state laws and have not been noted for adopting and enforcing strong local antipollution laws. On the contrary, state administrative agencies typically have had perennial difficulty in getting some municipalities to comply with state regulations in respect to sewage treatment and effluent disposal.

URBAN AND REGIONAL CONTROL

A considerable variety of local administrative arrangements for urban waste water management is found from state to state and within a single state. A recent treatise on the government of American urban areas lists five different patterns which are in wide use today:[4]

1. Municipal operation of both collection and treatment facilities.
2. Administration of the total sewerage system in all or most of an urban area by a special district government.
3. Operation by a series of special districts, often in combination with municipal systems.
4. Various contractual combinations.
5. Municipal operation of the local collection systems and special district management of the disposal facilities.

All too frequently the planning, operation, and financial management of these local and regional facilities fall short of reasonable levels of efficiency. Without the expanding state and federal programs of technical assistance, financial aid, and enforcement activity, the situation in many local areas and regions would be far worse than it is now. It is notable that the Water Quality Act of 1965 provides for a 10 per cent increase of a federal grant for construction of treatment facilities in the event that the project is properly certified as being in conformity with the comprehensive plan for a metropolitan or urban area. This kind of encouragement for regional planning could have important desirable consequences, direct and indirect, which could be cumulative over the years.

In this connection it is interesting to note that a major urban sewer district, grandly named the Municipality of Metropolitan Seattle, was originally intended to be a multipurpose municipal corporation to perform three functions, sewage disposal, public transportation, and comprehensive planning—for a large region. Only sewage disposal was approved originally in the spring of 1958 by the necessary dual majorities (in the central city and in the rest of the metropolitan area), and in 1962 a second try for public transportation failed when the proposal did not receive the required single overall majority of popular votes.[5] The fate of this kind of measure in the Seattle region and elsewhere suggests that neither a meaningful comprehensive regional planning enterprise nor even the less ambitious idea of integrated planning and administration for water supply and waste disposal is likely to be locally acceptable in the absence of incentives or requirements provided in state and/or federal programs.

Also worth noting here is the California arrangement in which primary responsibility for pollution administration lies with the state Water Quality Control Board, which, however, shares authority with nine regional water pollution control boards. Each of the latter boards develops its own pattern of general objectives and also prescribes specific requirements for disposal of effluents. The California program, like Wisconsin's, gives great emphasis to the case-by-case analysis of each local problem. The "objectives" are in the nature of general guidelines. The requirements are not regarded as rigid standards, and California "does not have statewide or even regionwide water-quality standards or the planned zoning of streams or underground basins."[6] Some of the policy issues centered around these matters will be examined later in connection with a discussion of the federal Water Quality Act of 1965.

INTERSTATE AND INTERSTATE-FEDERAL CONTROL

At this point, however, there should be at least brief mention of another and increasingly important category of organizations and arrangements which have developed in our rapidly complexifying federal system. These are the interstate and the interstate-federal organizations and arrangements of many varieties, both formal and informal. Some of them in the water field provide little more than occasional forums or communications networks, used frequently or little; some have genuine substance, others are largely ritual and facade. For example, the federal interagency river basin committees, with state representatives, have seldom been able to play a significant part in the processes of planning and policy making. Many observers doubt whether the possible river basin commissions, which may be established under the Water Resources Planning Act of 1965, could do a much better job of planning than have the interagency committees or the several temporary basin commissions established in special acts of Congress in recent years.

A more promising kind of interstate-federal organization for water planning and management is the Delaware River Basin Commission, established under a formal intergovernmental compact in 1961. The parties to the compact are the states of Delaware, New Jersey, New York, and Pennsylvania and the United States. Primary emphasis is placed on the commission's roles as comprehensive planner, coordinator, and promoter; but broad executive powers are also lodged with the commission. These latter powers provide a legal framework for regional action which could be utilized by the commission if state-local and federal agency actions leave unimplemented some significant parts of a comprehensive plan. Broad powers with respect to water quality management are included in the grant of authority to the commission. The combination of powers of planning and of implementation—for water development, allocation, and quality management—in an important interstate basin makes the Delaware commission unique among American government agencies in the water field. It is not perfect, of course, and it operates in practice under very real political constraints; but it does offer a model which the national government might well encourage for adaptation and use in other basins and regions. The national government could do worse, and frequently does.

FEDERAL CONTROL

The first general federal act to provide a basis for subsequent development of broad federal participation in water quality management was the temporary Water Pollution Control Act of 1948. A more comprehensive law was adopted in 1956, was strengthened by the amendments of 1961, and was further amended and broadened with the passage of the Water Quality Act of 1965. Federal activities in this field include a large research program, technical assistance and financial grants for state agency administrative programs, comprehensive basin surveys and plans for controlling water pollution, construction grants to aid municipalities to build waste treatment plants, promulgation of standards of water quality for interstate waters, and enforcement actions for the abatement of pollution of interstate or navigable waters. The 1965 act provided for the establishment of a new agency, the Federal Water Pollution Control Administration, in the Department of Health, Education, and Welfare, (transferred to the Department of the Interior in 1966), to be the primary federal agency concerned with water quality maintenance and improvement.

As might be expected, there appears to be little or no political controversy over the research and technical assistance programs. Considerable disagreement has been evident, however, concerning the size of the construction grant program and the limits on individual project grants. Some members of the minority party were opposed this year to increasing the construction grant authorization, and some who wanted to favor the smaller communities sought to keep low limits on the amount of any single federal grant. Governor Rockefeller, on the other hand, had good reason to favor not only a large increase of total federal funds but also the raising or elimination of the grant limits for a single project. Obviously, the developing mood of Congress and of the country favors heavy federal spending programs for pollution control.

WATER QUALITY STANDARDS APPROACH

The greatest disagreements evident in the 1965 congressional and other discussions focused on the water quality standards provisions of the bill by Senator Muskie of Maine (S. 4), which as amended became the Water Quality Act of 1965. A major purpose of those who favored the standards provisions apparently was to facilitate federal enforcement action in respect to pollution of interstate waters. The issues here are exceedingly complex and so is the statutory resolution. The new law provides that a state has one year after the enactment (October 2, 1965) to file a letter of intent that it will before June 30, 1967, adopt (1) water quality criteria applicable to interstate waters within the state and (2) a plan for implementation and enforcement of the criteria adopted. If the criteria and plan are so established and if the Secretary of the Interior determines that they serve the purposes of the act, such "State criteria and plan shall thereafter be the water quality standards applicable to such interstate waters or portions thereof." (Note that the state *criteria* would then become the water quality *standards*. But the secretary must determine that they are such as to protect the public health or welfare and to *enhance the quality of water*. The act provides that "in establishing such standards the Secretary, the Hearing Board, or the appropriate State authority shall take into consideration their use and value for public water supplies, propagation of fish and wildlife, recreational purposes, and agricultural, industrial, and other legitimate uses.")

If a state, however, does not file a letter of intent or does not establish water quality standards which the secretary finds acceptable, he may then prepare and publish regulations setting forth standards to be applicable to the waters in question. (The law says that "if the

Secretary or the Governor of any State affected by water quality standards established pursuant to this subsection desires a revision in such standards, the Secretary may, after reasonable notice and a conference of representatives of appropriate Federal departments and agencies, interstate agencies, States, municipalities and industries involved, prepare regulations. . . . ") The state is allowed another six months after publication by the secretary to adopt acceptable standards. Then, if a state fails so to act, the secretary shall promulgate the standards he has prepared—unless the governor of any affected state has petitioned (within 30 days after publication by the secretary) for a public hearing before a hearing board to be appointed by the secretary. There must be at least thirty days notice given of any such hearing. If the hearing board approves the standards as published by the secretary, the standards go into effect immediately. If the hearing board recommends revisions, the secretary is to promulgate revised regulations in accordance with the hearing board's recommendations, and those regulations become immediately effective.

Once all these hurdles are cleared or avoided and the standards are established (possibly about the end of 1968, earlier or later), then the "discharge of matter into such interstate waters or portions thereof, which reduces the quality of such waters below the water quality standards established . . . ," is subject to abatement action which may be initiated by the secretary. Federal action may be taken "whether the matter causing or contributing to such reduction is discharged directly into such waters or reaches such waters after discharge into tributaries of such waters. . . . " This "tributaries" provision would appear to be of great potential significance, though the same language was (and still is) part of another section of the law as it stood before the act of 1965. What is new is that the secretary presumably will not have to show that the polluting discharge is injurious or detrimental; presumably he will only have to show that the established water quality standards are not being met. Possibly the position of the federal authorities will thus be strengthened and enforcement will be made easier, but these outcomes may not be certain.

The enforcement procedures themselves are time consuming and complicated. Before the secretary may even request the Attorney General to start a suit, he must "notify the violators and other interested parties of the violation of such standards" at least 180 days before initiation of the abatement action. The act states that "the court shall receive in evidence a transcript of the proceedings of the conference and hearing provided for in this subsection [(c) of section 10], together with the recommendations of the conference and Hearing Board and the recommendations and standards promulgated by the Secretary, and such additional evidence, including that relating to the alleged violation of the standards, as it deems necessary to *a complete review of the standards* [emphasis supplied] and to a determination of all other issues relating to the alleged violation." Further: "The court, giving due consideration to the practicability and to the physical and economic feasibility of complying with such standards, shall have jurisdiction to enter such judgment and orders enforcing such judgment as the public interest and the equities of the case may require."

What the administrators, the lawyers, and the judges are likely to do with this law is not something for a mere economist to predict! It does seem clear, however, that the standards provisions of the new act are far from settling the vital specifics of what the standards shall be. We are apparently only at the beginning of a new phase of political-administrative bargainings and legal struggles which will test whether this kind of standards approach to the pollution problem is governmentally viable.

Many industrialists and many conservationists, for different reasons, have been unenthusiastic and doubtful about the standards approach generally and also about the setting of standards by federal authority. Dr. Curtis L. Newcombe, professor of biology at San Francisco State College and president of the California Conservation Council, commented aptly on these attitudes in his testimony before Senator Muskie's subcommittee in June, 1965:[7]

> The term "water quality standards" is used and misused increasingly as public awareness of pollution grows. Unfortunately, the term is seized upon by some sincere and conscientious advocates of eliminating and preventing pollution as an easy panacea to all our water quality problems. On the other hand I suspect that others more concerned with keeping down the cost of expanding industry and agriculture, regardless of its consequences, shrewdly promote inadequate standards as a means for acquiring a "license to pollute" such as has been the case frequently with the procedure of stream classification.
>
> Steps toward establishing water quality standards for the purpose of abating or preventing pollution rather than providing a license to a discharger to dispose of his wastes in the most convenient and inexpensive manner are scientifically complex and administratively difficult.

The chief federal enforcement officer, Murray Stein, responded to a question by Senator Muskie with a comment that is pertinent at this point:[8]

> I think we are adequately staffed for the enforcement operation. If we have the responsibility for standards; no, we are not. The one big danger, Senator—I have pointed this out before—is to get the whole staff working on establishing standards of water quality to the exclusion of enforcement operations. I think we have to do both, and, if we are going to keep up our

momentum in enforcement and we have the responsibility for standards, we would have need for more staff.

Here lie some quite practical questions. Can adequate professional staff be provided? Will Congress appropriate sufficient funds? Are there enough properly trained persons in the country who can perform satisfactorily in the new positions which will need to be created?

During the June, 1965, hearings Senator Muskie took occasion to comment on some of the criticisms of the standards approach:[9]

> First, in your criticism directed against hasty standards. . . . As a matter of fact, our procedures, I think, as set out in our bill, constitute assurance that there would be no hasty standards.
>
> Secondly, you are against standards that license pollution, and so am I, and so is the bill. As a matter of fact, the bill carefully states, and in explicit language, which I think is beyond doubt, that the statutes should be used to enhance water quality; that there should be a positive mandate statement of the law which could not be evaded without a direct and overt violation of it. . . .
>
> Thirdly, I would say that the purpose of the standards in the Federal bill, S. 4, is to establish not a ceiling of water quality, but a floor, and from this point of view, it seems to me that the sooner we establish the floor, the better off we are going to be, because at the present stage, too many of our representatives feel that the floor is dropping rapidly. We want to put a floor in before we get to the bottom.
>
> And, finally in the State of Maine we established a classification of water, made, I think, in 1952 (1962?), and it was used initially to identify the current status of water quality and all main (Maine?) waters.
>
> Five years later, which is not, I think, an unconscionable period, we embarked on a program of upgrading our water, in other words, raising the floor. And there is where . . . they have developed programs of upgrading which have been endorsed by the legislature and have imposed heavy financial burdens upon communities and upon industries.
>
> I am fighting for this now, though I grant you that some of those who supported the Maine water classifications in the first instance did so with some of the improper connotations which you suggested in your statement. It can be used either way. But so can any water quality law. If you have poorly motivated administrators, they are going to destroy any water quality legislation that you write down on the books. But I think that the water standards approach can be used to have a rapidly upgraded water quality in a way that will be beyond reproach.

So much for the "standards approach" for the moment. Now, what are the technical means which may be used in order to achieve reasonably high standards of water quality?

POLLUTION CONTROL SYSTEMS

It is now technically possible to treat most municipal and industrial waste waters so as to bring them back to levels of quality which, in all known essential respects, are equal or superior to the quality levels before use. The trouble is, of course, that existing advanced treatment technology cannot be applied outside the laboratory to achieve such results for municipal and industrial waste waters except at costs which are almost literally out of this world. Fortunately, there are various technical measures other than treatment of waste waters which may be used in order to protect and enhance the quality of surface waters and groundwaters. Among the other methods are dilution, reaeration, temporary storage and programmed release of wastes, changing industrial production processes and products, and recovery of wastes, sometimes for profitable reuse or sale in by-products. The engineering and economic problem here is to select the best (or a satisfactory) combination of measures to achieve specified levels of water quality at least cost.

The political and governmental problem is even harder. It involves the continual making and remaking of complex sets of decisions about what levels of water quality should be maintained, where, when, and how. This decision making involves the estimating of those benefits and costs which are not measured in dollar amounts in market transactions. The political problem also extends to questions of who should get the benefits, who should pay the costs, and to the kinds of incentives to be built into the government programs.

At least three basic kinds of measures for implementing governmental decisions to maintain or improve water quality may be distinguished.[10] First, there is direct regulation; and the formal, explicit setting of water quality standards may or may not be a part of a system of direct regulation. Second, there are grants or payments from the federal and/or state governments. Third, there are charges which may be levied for the treatment of wastes *and* for the disposal of effluents or other pollutants directly or indirectly into public waters.

The existing systems for water pollution control in this country typically utilize measures from all three of these basic categories. Regulations, grants, and charges are not necessarily alternative means of implementation in a pollution control system; they may be and are being used together, and almost certainly they will continue to be so used. Nevertheless, there are some very real and fundamental policy issues concerning what should be the appropriate "mix" of the different kinds of devices. Most current thinking runs to the ideas of stricter direct regulation and a massive program of federal grants plus state grants in some states. The billion dollar bond issue approved in November, 1965, in New York State indicates that voters there favored very large state grants for construction of municipal waste treatment facilities.

Unfortunately, relatively little attention has been given so far to the idea that effluent charges could be a major element in an efficient and equitable system for pollution control. We have had a

Keynesian revolution in economic theory, but a Kneeseian revolution in economic policies for pollution control is yet to come. Nevertheless, Allen Kneese's proposal[11] that effluent charges should be a central feature of regional systems for water quality management is an exceedingly important proposal and deserves widespread and serious study. The effluent charges to be levied on polluters would be based carefully on the downstream damages and opportunity costs attributable to the upstream waste disposal. A key virtue of a well-administered effluent charges system is that it provides real financial incentives for municipal and industrial waste dischargers to approximate the "economically proper" levels of treatment, to seek optimal process and product adjustments which take account of "spillover" costs, and to make more appropriate industrial location decisions. All these kinds of decisions would tend to be taken in the light of the full and real costs of waste disposal, just as ordinary business decisions are made in the light of the costs of labor and materials and other factors of production. Direct federal and state regulation would no doubt still be necessary, but it could be a very much smaller element in the total system. The primary part would be the semiautomatic subsystem of administered prices or effluent charges. Direct and indirect grants and subsidies to municipal and industrial waste dischargers could be substantially smaller than would otherwise be considered possible or desirable.

Worth noting in this connection is the fact that the Environmental Pollution Panel of the President's Science Advisory Committee issued a major report (November, 1965) in which it recommended that consideration be given to a "tax-like" system of effluent charges. Such a system, the panel pointed out, could provide economic incentives for controlling pollution of the environment by those who have found it profitable so far to get rid of their wastes by dumping them into the air or into rivers and lakes.[12]

Whatever may be the "mix" of institutional arrangements and financial devices in the evolving pollution control systems of the several states and regions, there can be little doubt that there is a great need for regional planning for water quality management. Such planning ordinarily could best be carried on as part of a broader activity, regional water resources planning. And of course water planning by itself makes little sense unless it is adequately related to, or is made an integral part of, the still broader enterprise of regional planning generally. Good water plans must fit in with land use plans,[13] outdoor recreation facility plans, transportation plans, financial plans, and so on. Ordinarily, water planning can best be done on a river basin or watershed basis, but the larger basins cut across the boundaries of local and state governmental units. What is needed is a variety of governmental and intergovernmental planning agencies for small and large basins, both intrastate and interstate.

Here lie some of the great challenges of our years. The quality of our natural environment affects the quality of human life, subtly and powerfully, for good or for ill. We may well ask, for what shall it profit man if he dominate the whole earth and yet befoul and lose his natural home?

NOTES

1. David Braybrooke and Charles E. Lindblom, *A Strategy of Decision* (New York, The Free Press of Glencoe, 1963), p. 247, n. 8.
2. The words quoted are from Jack Edward McKee and Harold W. Wolf (eds.), *Water Quality Criteria*, 2nd ed. (Sacramento, The Resources Agency of California, State Water Quality Control Board, 1963), p. 29. The following brief discussion of the bases of state programs is largely adapted from Chapter III of this lengthy (548-page), valuable study.
3. *Ibid.*, p. 29.
4. John C. Bollens and Henry J. Schmandt, *The Metropolis* (New York, Harper and Row, 1965), p. 326.
5. *Ibid.*, p. 451.
6. McKee and Wolf, p. 2. See also p. 34.
7. *Hearings*, Water Pollution, Special Subcommittee on Air and Water Pollution, Committee on Public Works, Senate, Eighty-ninth Cong., 1st Sess., May-June, 1965, Part 2, p. 640.
8. *Ibid.*, Part 1, p. 119.
9. *Ibid.*, Part 2, pp. 648–49. Senator Muskie directed his remarks particularly to Dr. Curtis L. Newcombe, some of whose testimony is quoted above.
10. Cf. Allen V. Kneese, *The Economics of Regional Water Quality Management* (Baltimore, The Johns Hopkins Press, 1964), pp. 192–97. Research and the diffusion of knowledge are, of course, even more "basic" than the kinds of implementation measures distinguished here.
11. *Ibid.*
12. *New York Times*, Nov. 7, 1965.
13. An exceedingly difficult and little understood set of water pollution problems is traceable in considerable part to the runoff to lakes and streams from both rural and urban lands. Soil, pesticides, and plant nutrients are carried into the streams and lakes, algae and weed nuisance conditions are created or made worse, and the "aging" processes of these water bodies are greatly accelerated. Land use regulations or "land effluent charges" may be needed to deal effectively with these aspects of water quality degradation.

PART 2

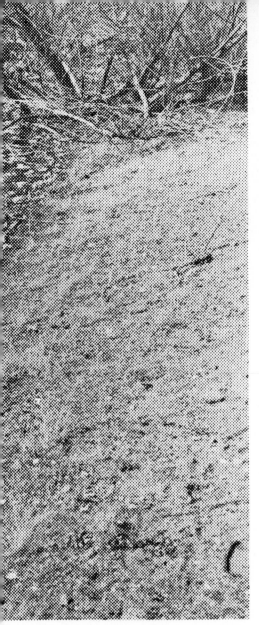

"Winter kill" takes its toll: oxygen-starved fish die in shallow, enriched lakes during ice-covered months. Spring thaws reveal this carnage along the shore of Lake Odessa.

THE IOWA SITUATION

CHAPTER 6

THE WATER POLLUTION SITUATION AND CONTROLS

ROBERT L. MORRIS

IT IS DECLARED IN THE IOWA WATER POLLUTION CONTROL ACT (1965) that it is public policy to conserve the waters of the state and to protect, maintain, and improve its quality for public water supplies, propagation of wildlife, fish and aquatic life, and for domestic, agricultural, industrial, recreational, and other legitimate uses. No waste is to be discharged into waters of our state without first being given a degree of treatment necessary to protect the legitimate uses of such waters. It is also stated public policy to provide for the prevention, abatement, and control of new, increasing, potential, or existing water pollution. The Water Pollution Control Act (1965) signed into law by Governor Harold E. Hughes also created a Water Pollution Control Commission consisting of nine members as follows:

1. The commissioner of public health.
2. The director of the state conservation commission.
3. The director of the Iowa natural resources council.
4. A member from the staff of one of the state universities who has technical background, training, and knowledge in the field of water pollution.
5. The secretary of agriculture.
6. Four (4) electors of the state who shall be selected from the state at large solely with regard to their qualifications and fitness to discharge the duties of office without regard to their political affiliation. Of these four (4) one (1) shall

ROBERT L. MORRIS is assistant director, State Hygienic Laboratory of Iowa, University of Iowa, Iowa City, Iowa.

represent industry, one (1) shall represent municipal government, one (1) shall be an owner-operator farmer and one (1) shall represent the public at large. The chairman is selected annually by a vote of the commission members.

The commission, through the state Department of Health, shall have general supervision over administration and enforcement of all laws relating to the pollution of any waters of the state except those in instances where a public health emergency exists, wherein the state Department of Health has direct authority in its own right. The commission shall develop comprehensive plans and programs for the prevention, control, and abatement of new, increasing, potential, or existing pollution of the waters of the state. The commission shall also move toward adoption of reasonable quality standards for the waters of the state, in relation to the public use to which they are put, as it shall deem necessary for the purposes of the Water Pollution Control Act.

The designated membership of the Water Pollution Control Commission provides strong representation of all the interested areas with respect to water quality and wisely retains within the structure of the Iowa State Department of Health the engineering, scientific, and technical responsibility for carrying out the policies and programs of the Water Pollution Control Commission. It is felt that this new Water Pollution Control Act, creating a broad spectrum commission working through the state Department of Health, provides a very adequate organizational nucleus to delineate and solve the problems of water pollution control which face the state of Iowa.

Pollution can be defined as the contamination of any waters of the state so as to create a nuisance or render such waters unclean, noxious, or impure so as to be actually harmful, detrimental, or injurious to public health, safety, or welfare to domestic, commercial, industrial, agricultural, or recreational use or to livestock, wild animals, birds, fish, or other aquatic life. A broad approach to the types of pollution results in categories such as the following:

1. *Natural pollution.* Silt or turbidities flushed off the surface of the soil at runoff periods and high organic load from decayed vegetation produce adverse conditions for aquatic life as well as natural tastes and odors in surface water supplies. Changes in agricultural cultivation practices have intensified this type of natural pollution.

2. *Human wastes.* These domestic wastes are primarily carbonaceous and nitrogenous in character and their most serious adverse effect is rapid and extensive utilization of natural dissolved oxygen in streams and groundwaters.

Also, human wastes can be carriers of pathogenic organisms, including the viruses.

3. *Industrial wastes.* This type of waste in Iowa has been for the most part carbonaceous in character resulting in dissolved oxygen depletion in our streams. Also, the number of metal processing industries in some areas of our state have produced adverse concentrations of cyanides and various heavy metals. Recently, increasing production of nitrogenous fertilizers has brought this type of industrial pollution to significant levels.

4. *Agricultural wastes.* Extensive cultivation of our soil surfaces has increased the turbidity levels of many of our streams, and the concentration of livestock feeding with attendant pileup of animal offal has concentrated this type of problem so that it now becomes a significant hazard to some small streams and impoundments. The use of vast tonages of pesticides and artificial chemical fertilizers has brought agricultural waste to an increased level of significance in Iowa's water pollution problem.

We are a relatively small state having somewhat less than 3 million people widely dispersed over our entire area. We are also blessed with a considerable number of good-sized intrastate streams as well as two great rivers on our eastern and western boundaries. Because we fortunately have a large proportion of high-quality agricultural land, the influx of many types of industry has been slow in Iowa and most of our processing industries are tied in one way or another to our agricultural economy. Many states in the eastern part of our country and on the West Coast have been confronted with diverse industrial waste problems which are just beginning to make themselves evident in Iowa. Therefore, we should make every effort to benefit by the experiences with large concentrations of both population and industry as they have affected the quality of streams and groundwaters.

NEED FOR WATER QUALITY CONTROL

Increased awareness of the problem of water quality and water pollution control has arisen in the past decade for a variety of logical reasons. The population of our state has been increasing and changing its traditional location. People are moving off the farm and into cities at an ever increasing rate necessitating constant review of domestic waste handling facilities. This movement off the farm has resulted from increased technology such as mechanization and the use of pesticides, herbicides, and chemical fertilizers. Under our present level of agricultural development, modern large-unit farms could not function without the use of these mechanical and chemical aids. The quantity and quality of practically all the foodstuffs to which we have been accustomed would degrade and soon become unavailable. The die is cast; we must learn to live in the type of agricultural society which has developed.

The influx of people from the rural areas to Iowa cities has provided a readily available labor market of comparatively high quality, and this fact is always a major factor in the decision of industrial concerns to locate in Iowa. In several areas of our state, both surface water and groundwater of good to excellent quality exists which is attractive to wet-process industries. Many Iowa communities are located on existing major transportation systems for air, rail, highway, and navigable streams and our state is in the center of a large commodity marketing area. We can expect the movement of many types of industry into Iowa in the future, bringing with them new water pollution problems.

Many of the complaints about water quality in our streams and lakes arise from our modern way of life. Industrial development resulting in shorter work weeks has given the average individual more recreation time. He demands more from his streams and lakes and is much more sophisticated in his individual desire for water quality. Credit buying power in the hands of the average man has introduced him to the pleasures of power boating, sailing, water skiing, and increased fishing time, as well as camping and picnicking. These economic factors have placed a greater proportion of our Iowa population on our waterways than ever before. It is also quite commonplace for the average Iowan to travel to other states where isolated vacation areas frequently have entirely different water pollution problems resulting in better quality streams for many of his recreational outlets. He comes back home demanding the same quality of recreational water and does not always realize that multiple usage of Iowa water presents a very complex problem of quality control.

EXTENT OF SEWAGE TREATMENT

What is the water quality status of our streams, lakes, and groundwater at the present time? Considering the many different uses for our water, we are fortunate that the flowing streams and impoundments of our state are in a relatively clean condition. Our streams are not flowing "sewers" as they are in certain areas of some other states. There are approximately 7,500 miles of flowing fishable streams in the state of Iowa, and fish kills have been reported on only 350 miles of these streams. Usually, these fish kills are concentrated in industrial areas or below population-overloaded municipal sewage plants.

There are 944 municipalities in the state of Iowa and about 465 of them are served by municipal sewers. This calculates to be approximately 93 per cent of the urban population of Iowa. Four hundred and twenty-four of these towns have domestic sewage treatment of some type, representing sewage treatment for 91 per cent of Iowa towns having municipal sewer systems. Actually, 91 per cent of the total urban population is served by municipal sewage treatment plants. These figures are approximate but they indicate the extensive effort that individual cities and the Iowa State Department of Health has made in the past in grappling with the water pollution control problem. This is a far better record than exists in most other states.

One must remember, however, that the efficiency of sewage treatment is vitally important and he should not be deluded by simple arithmetic alone. Primary treatment removes about 30 per cent of the organic load in domestic sewage as solids, while secondary treatment removes roughly 90 per cent. The efficiency with which the sewage plant is operated also governs the waste load which is placed upon the receiving stream. Good sewage plant design must consider the receiving capacity of the stream into which the plant effluent is discharged. Primary, or 30 per cent, treatment may be quite acceptable if the plant effluent is discharged into a stream having very adequate dilution characteristics and, conversely, even secondary or complete treatment may be unsatisfactory for a large town discharging its waste into a small stream with inadequate dilution characteristics.

Many Iowa municipal sewage treatment plants are seriously overloaded and some of them have equipment which no longer operates as efficiently as originally designed. Population increases and the ravages of time on the mechanical equipment have produced this effect and it is showing up in elevated organic loading in some of our streams.

Federal funds coming into the Iowa State Department of Health have had an extremely beneficial effect on stimulating municipalities to build new plants or to expand and rejuvenate their overloaded or antiquated existing facilities. The federal Water Quality Act signed into law in 1965 increased the funds available for municipal assistance in construction of sewage treatment facilities, and the forseeable future holds the probability of catching up with the plant construction phases of water pollution control.

STATUS OF WATER QUALITY IN IOWA

Our present understanding of the actual quality of our streams, lakes, and groundwaters is not as good as it should be. In most areas of the public health problem we are quite adequate in the protection of the water supply for potable use. However, viral diseases are alleged to be transmittable by water supplies and Iowa like most other states has essentially no surveillance program for these pathogenic organisms. While we have statewide analytical programs for trace organic materials such as detergents, pesticides, and taste producing compounds, the magnitude of this problem analytically is great and our capacity to meet it is unfortunately too small. The quality of our streams and lakes with respect to their fish culturing characteristics is almost unknown, as there are no programs in existence to measure the long-range eutrophication rates in our streams and lakes. Greater usage of fertilizers is resulting in an increased level of nitrate (NO_3) and phosphorus in many of our streams. Concentration of these two important plant nutrients in our streams is also being elevated by the increasing population using our domestic municipal treatment plants. Domestic sewage treatment, even when efficiently designed and operated, introduces stabilized nitrate (NO_3) and phosphates into our streams. These two chemical ingredients serve as increased nutrients for growth of algae and other biological organisms which are necessary elements in the fish-food chain. While this fact may on the surface appear to be a beneficial situation, it must be remembered that excessive growth of algae, *Actinomycetes,* and other biological organisms often produce adverse tastes and odors in water supplies. Also, when these extensive biological growths "die off" in the water, massive depletion of oxygen, with resultant fish kill, often results.

It is one thing to recognize program shortcomings; it will be an extensive and expensive task to overcome them. Increased surveillance in the areas just mentioned will require more sanitary engineers and scientists for both field and laboratory work as well as sanitarians to assist the engineers in sample collection for field studies. Scientists and engineers are difficult and expensive to obtain, and we will have to learn to utilize these highly trained individuals to their fullest technical capabilities by giving them the assistance of technicians in the laboratory and sanitarians in the field.

We have always felt that our precious groundwater supplies were safe from water pollution problems, but the past few years have taught us that we will have to make a conscious effort if our subterranean water supplies are to remain safe from contamination. We have learned that wastes flowing in our streams and distributed promiscuously on the surface of the ground can reach shallow groundwater aquifers in concentrations sufficient to seriously degrade the quality of the groundwater supply. The use of nitrogenous fertilizers, to maintain high agricultural nutritive quality of our soils, is resulting in significant increases in the nitrate (NO_3) content of our shallow groundwater wells, and the number of rural shallow water supplies exceeding acceptable nitrate ion limits is rapidly on the increase. One major stream supplying a municipal water supply in our state used to have a nitrate (NO_3) content of 5 milligrams per liter. It is not uncommon now to find as high as 40 milligrams per liter of nitrate (NO_3) in this stream following surface runoff periods. We have evidence that shallow wells located along streams with elevated nitrate contents have shown increased nitration in many cases.

While the level of chlorinated hydrocarbon pesticides in our larger flowing streams has to date been extremely low, with increased usage of these highly durable materials, it is only a question of time before the levels of these allegedly toxic materials begins to rise in our streams to a measurably significant point. We already have some evidence to indicate that surface-applied pesticide is beginning to reach shallow groundwater aquifers in certain types of soils.

CONTROL MEASURES

What must we do now if we are to arrest and reverse this trend toward increased chemical and biological content in our streams, lakes, and groundwaters? First, we must increase surveillance of the environment and our watercourses in order to delineate more efficiently actual conditions and quality fluctuations. This means increased engineering in the design of stream and lake surveys, much more field sampling, and a considerable increase in laboratory examinations on the specimens collected. In order to do this efficiently, Iowa needs a mobile laboratory with trained chemists to work with the field engineers, especially in the western and northwestern parts of Iowa. Closer educational work with plant operators and greater operational efficiency of existing sewage treatment plants will do much toward reducing the strength of domestic wastes to which our streams are subjected. The recent Mandatory Certification Act for sewage plant operators passed by the 1965 legislature will certainly result in better sewage plant operation in our state. The Iowa Water Pollution Control Federation and the Iowa Water Works Association should be complimented on the forthright vigor which they displayed in obtaining this certification law.

If we are really going to move toward better quality streams, we must have criteria on which to base our evaluation. This means the establishment of stream quality standards and effluent standards so that the best possible usage of the stream is achieved. This is the task of the newly created Water Pollution Control Commission, and you may be assured that the commission recognizes the magnitude and importance of this task.

Research and development of new and better waste treatment or utilization processes will have to be achieved if we expect to triumph over the problem of increasing amounts and complexities of both domestic and industrial wastes. Actually, there have been no significant breakthroughs in the methods by which organic wastes are degraded before discharge into streams. We used to feel that all we had to do was render the waste liquid and stabilize it against rapid oxygen demand. Now we know that this is not enough because the stable, non-oxygen demanding nitrates and phosphates are resulting in increased eutrophication of our streams and lakes to the point where biologically oriented water quality people are becoming alarmed. The federal government has recognized this important phase of the problem and is doing everything possible to stimulate research in this area.

We must develop a better understanding of the adverse effects of allegedly toxic materials so that our maximum permissible concentration values are scientifically realistic. We are presently concerned about "zero tolerance" of materials for which we had no adequate, sensitive, analytical test as little as two or three years ago. A short time ago we were able to test for certain critical pesticides as low as 1 part per million, but now we can analyze for these same materials in parts per trillion. In other words, we are approximately a million times more efficient analytically than we were a few short years ago in the pesticide analysis problem. Does the simple fact that we can now detect concentrations that were undetectable before mean that the material is suddenly a toxic hazard? Obviously, this is not at all the true indication, but it is often being interpreted in that manner on a legal basis. The better the analytical chemist becomes, the more complex the legal problem will become. The development of fundamental reliable toxicological data on potential adverse effects of many of the commonly used pesticides and other exotic chemicals is one of the most difficult problems facing scientists today. The collecting of physiological and pathological data on the effects of these trace materials on mankind is so complex that it is almost stupefying in magnitude. Here is the area where reason, logic, and common sense will have to be balanced with scientific research of the most sophisticated nature. Because we have had no actual toxicological data on certain suspicious ingredients, the maximum permissible concentration has been assigned as that level represented by the lowest concentration detectable analytically. Either we will have to cease introducing some of these obviously beneficial agricultural chemicals into our environment, or we will have to say to ourselves, "This is a level we will accept as a calculated risk consistent with the benefits achieved."

It is not uncommon for municipal and state development groups to work with great vigor in order to attract industrial concerns to locate in their area. Great care and engineering logic should be used in such a process so that the industries attracted do not create industrial waste problems incompatible with the assimilation facilities existing at the proposed location. No city should desire an industry which creates waste disposal problems of greater magnitude than the economic benefits its presence brings to the community. The logistics of waste disposal has frequently been ill-considered in our country; and industries regretfully have been located in areas not particularly well suited to their individual specific requirements. If this phase of industry placement is adequately perused prior to the final location decision, Iowa will be spared many of the problems of water pollution control that have seriously plagued other states.

A combination of favorable factors presently has given us a good position in the water pollution control situation. This is due primarily to a modest population growth, the inherent common sense and decency of our citizens, and to a long-time effort on the part of a small nucleus of dedicated engineers and scientists who have accomplished much with little. The "do unto others as you would have them do unto you" attitude of many Iowa industries and municipalities has given us our presently tolerable status. It could have been much worse, but we certainly cannot continue to let this problem take care of itself by fortunate happenstance. We have a good organizational and technical nucleus with which to meet this water quality challenge successfully, but the people of Iowa must recognize that increased water quality under our individual situation will cost money. It will mean increased budget for the water pollution section of the Iowa State Department of Health and the State Hygienic Laboratory which performs the laboratory services. Industries and municipalities will have to devote significant sums to construction of expanded and new facilities for waste treatment. The agricultural community will have to develop more acceptable usage methods for the exotic organics so necessary to their modern economy, and they will have to recognize their responsibility to minimize as much as feasible the contamination of our water sources. The people of Iowa are going to have to "really want" improved water quality rather than simply give the problem lip service. We can have anything we are willing to support.

CHAPTER 7

WASTEWATER DISPOSAL PRACTICES AND CONTROLS

PAUL J. HOUSER

BEFORE MAN SET FOOT ON THE LANDS OF IOWA MANY YEARS AGO, THE surface and groundwaters were already contaminated. One can find in the literature mention of herds of buffalo forging streams with some of the animals becoming mired in the mud and dying when their struggles to free themselves were unsuccessful. Undoubtedly, decaying vegetation and other organic matter were washed into the streams or percolated into the groundwaters causing objectionable tastes and odors. But it was not until man came with his municipal, industrial, and agricultural developments that the contamination from land runoff and the discharge of waste waters became pollution—meaning that the contamination increased to the extent that it was detrimental to downstream uses and, therefore, a violation of the riparian rights doctrine.

In this chapter are presented some facts and figures, taken from the files of the state Department of Health, regarding the pollution situation in Iowa and a discussion of control measures.

MUNICIPAL SEWERAGE PRACTICES

The number of municipalities in Iowa having systems installed for the purpose of collecting and disposing of sewage, and the number of these municipalities which had treatment facilities on June 30, 1965, and the population served by these sewage collection and treatment facilities are given in Table 7.1. The figures show the breakdown according to population groups and total population served by these

PAUL J. HOUSER is chief, Environmental Hygiene and Engineering Services, Iowa State Department of Health, Des Moines, Iowa.

98

Table 7.1 Municipal Sewerage Systems in Iowa* (Based on 1960 Population June 30, 1965).

Population	Total Number of Municipalities		Municipalities With Sanitary Sewers		Municipalities Treating Sewage		Total Population Treated to Total Sewered Population (per cent)
	No.	Population	No.	Population	No.	Population	
Over 15,000	20	995,125	20	995,125	20	995,125	100.0
2,000–15,000 ...	108	498,962	107	493,224	104	482,183	97.8
1,000–2,000	110	148,795	106	144,282	91	124,494	86.3
500–1,000	211	146,271	162	116,270	148	106,584	91.7
Under 500	495	120,208	70	25,007	61	21,642	86.5
Totals	944	1,909,361	465	1,773,908	424	1,730,028	97.5

NOTE: Two sanitary districts in unincorporated communities and two other unincorporated communities (approximate population of 1960 persons) not included.

*Compiled by Division of Public Health Engineering, State Department of Health, Des Moines, Iowa.

99

facilities. It is significant that 97.5 per cent of the population served by sewers is also served by treatment facilities. Also, note the distribution of these facilities. This is quite a good record in comparison to some of the other states, particularly those more heavily populated than Iowa. Figure 7.1 shows the progress that has been made toward the installation of municipal sewage treatment plants for the population served by sewage collection systems.

This tabulation does not reflect the adequacy of municipal sewage collection and treatment facilities. Several of the treatment plants included are not supplying satisfactory treatment. Some are providing only primary treatment, that is, the removal of only settleable and floatable solids. Although this is adequate in some places, it may not be adequate in others.

Personnel of the state Department of Health have contributed data to a conference of state sanitary engineers' report to the federal Water Pollution Control Administration on the needs for municipal water pollution control projects. These data demonstrated the essentiality of new treatment plants and enlargement of existing plants which were known to be overloaded or otherwise providing inadequate treatment and indicated the old plants that were obsolete or not dependable to provide adequate treatment throughout the year. The recommended needs presented in the last report were as follows: 41 new plants for treatment of raw sewage, 66 enlargement or replacement projects, and 6 plants for new sewer systems for a total of 113 projects. These recommended needs do not imply that a condition of pollution exists below the outlets as defined in the Iowa law, but they do imply that the effluents should be improved so as to provide a higher quality of water in the receiving streams.

The 1956 enactment by Congress which provided funds for grants to construct municipal sewage treatment facilities was, and continues to be, a stimulus for their installation and improvement. These funds provide 30 per cent of the cost of constructing interceptor sewers and treatment plants. The initial maximum of $250,000 for any one project was later raised to $600,000 and was more recently raised to $1,200,000. Cost of land is not included. During the 9 years since these funds were available, a total of 29 new plants and 106 enlargements or replacements of existing plants were constructed or are now under construction. The total amount of grant money was $10,600,000 and the total cost of construction was approximately $62,500,000. Unfortunately, the allotments to Iowa over this period of years were not sufficient to include all projects for which applications had been submitted, with the result that construction of some projects was delayed until funds were available.

In addition to the projects constructed with financial aid during

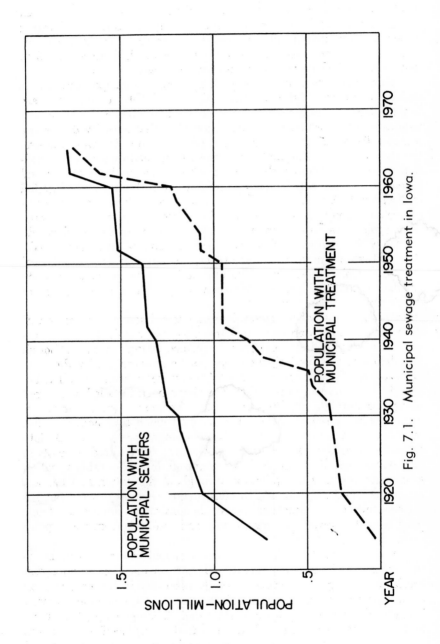

Fig. 7.1. Municipal sewage treatment in Iowa.

this 9-year period, 96 projects were installed without aid, 78 of which are serving sewage collection systems. Although industries discharging wastes into municipal sewers receive an indirect benefit from this financial aid when treatment facilities are installed, there is no aid to industries for installation of facilities with separate outlets.

There are other causes of pollution from municipal sources. It will be noted from Table 7.1 that only 465 of 944 municipalities are listed as having sanitary sewers. This leaves a difference of 479 municipalities, some of which may have drain lines that actually do convey sewage. These drains may not have been installed for this purpose, but they were available and connections were made when new buildings were constructed in the area or when other methods of disposal failed to function satisfactorily. Some of these drains were installed under provisions of the drainage laws and, according to our legal counsel, connections to field drains for the purpose of conveying sewage are illegal. How many municipalities have sewers of this kind we do not know, but we frequently receive complaints of insanitary conditions below their outlets. In some cases, the situation has caused local officials to replace these drains with properly installed sewers, or action has been taken by the state Department of Health under provisions of the Stream Pollution Law.

Another cause of pollution from municipal sewer systems results from the overflow from combined sewers—those installed for the purpose of conveying both sewage and surface runoff waters. Although installation of this type of sewer has not been permitted by the state Department of Health for at least thirty-five years, some installed before that time remain in use. Overflows have been installed to prevent sewage backup into buildings when the sewers are flowing over capacity. Likewise, overflows have been installed when treatment facilities were constructed to permit diluted raw sewage to be discharged into a nearby stream or watercourse. This was necessary to reduce costs to reasonable amounts. Congress has recognized this undesirable situation as contributing to water pollution throughout the nation and has appropriated funds, not for aid in constructing separate sewers but for further study of the situation and for demonstration projects to determine ways to prevent or control pollution resulting from these practices.

A third cause of pollution from municipal sewerage systems is the bypassing of treatment facilities during construction or operation breakdowns. Bypass sewers are usually necessary in the construction of treatment plants but, in some cases, they are too conveniently used because of the lack of proper maintenance. In other cases, they must be used when equipment is being repaired or replaced or when enlargement of the treatment facilities is under construction. Control of bypassing is a difficult problem confronting all water pollution control agencies.

INDUSTRIAL WASTE TREATMENT PRACTICES

Other wastes causing water pollution are those resulting from industrial processing—the so-called "wet industries." Quite a variety of these industries exists in Iowa, notably those processing food and kindred products. At present there are fifty-four wet-process industries in Iowa which have their own treatment facilities, varying from retention basins for release of wastes during high stream flows to elaborate plants providing a high degree of treatment. However, a few industries are operating without adequate treatment facilities. Notable are the small butter and cheese manufacturing plants that have been in existence for quite a number of years. According to the latest listing by the state Department of Agriculture, there are 196 milk processing plants, including those for butter and cheese manufacturing, in the state. Process wastes from most of these are discharged into municipal sewers, but wastes from others are discharged into watercourses by separate outlets. The exact number of the latter is not known. The limited staff of the state Department of Health is unable to conduct stream pollution investigations until complaints are received concerning nuisance conditions or damage to fish life. One cause for complaints is occasioned by the change in manufactured products in these industries. During the past several years some of the smaller creameries have consolidated for the manufacturing of butter and others have changed to the manufacturing of cheese. The latter activity has resulted in a significant change in the waste characteristics in that whey is included in the waste flow and this greatly increases the pollution load discharged into the receiving stream.

Creating continuing problems in stream pollution control is the meat slaughtering and processing industry. Decentralization has been taking place in this industry and quite a number of new plants have been constructed in Iowa. During the past ten years twelve of these plants were constructed with separate outlets. Unfortunately, some of these are located on relatively small streams with very little flow for dilution of their wastes. This means they must incorporate good waste salvaging methods, maintain good housekeeping, and provide a high degree of waste treatment. But even so the residual pollution load from the waste treatment process is greater than desirable for a high quality of water in the receiving stream and in some cases has resulted in conditions of pollution.

On the other side of the ledger is the improvement in quality of some of our streams due to a reduction in the number of other kinds of food processing plants. In the past sweet-corn canning was one of the industries causing severe conditions of stream pollution. Closing of most of these plants has eliminated this particular problem of waste disposal.

In the meantime other new industries have located in Iowa with complicated waste products and methods of preventing stream pollution. Notable among these is the increased manufacture and blending of fertilizers. Sufficient concentrations of certain elements in the wastes are known to be toxic to fish life. However, treatment processes to reduce this toxicity are not practical within the limit of reasonable costs. It is, therefore, necessary to install holding basins for discharging the wastes into the flowing stream at rates that will not cause pollution. With the effort being made to introduce new and diversified industries into Iowa and with the change in processes and materials used in existing industrial operations, we will be forced to cope with new problems in waste disposal and water pollution control.

DILUTION

Insofar as both municipal and industrial sources of pollution are concerned, it must be borne in mind that a flowing stream will provide for dilution only the quantity of water which the drainage area and its tributaries will provide. During periods of low flow this amount may not be sufficient for assimilating the residual pollution even after the wastes have been subjected to as high a degree of treatment as practical. In the design of new or enlarged treatment plants we have not adopted the theory that dilution is the solution to pollution. But we do recognize the fact that it is practically impossible to treat all wastes for complete removal of all traces of pollutional substances. New treatment plants must be designed to provide adequate treatment for effluent to be discharged into streams during periods of low flow as determined by the records. But we also recognize that if and when the stream flow is actually below the design flow, a condition of undesirable contamination or even pollution, as defined in the law, may result. Unfortunately, in Iowa as in most other states, too much water goes under the bridge during some days of the year and too little goes under during others. What we need is a leveling out of these flows so that there is a sufficient amount of water for dilution of adequately treated wastes on all days of the year.

CAUSES OF FISH KILLS

Fish kills have been reported in approximately 350 miles of the 7,500 miles of flowing, fishable streams in Iowa. During the last five years, according to reports submitted by state Conservation Commission employees, there was a total of seventy-six reported kills in the following categories:

1. Caused by continuous industrial waste discharges—18.
2. Caused by continuous municipal sewage discharges—8.
3. Caused by industrial waste spills, either accidental or from careless operations—13.
4. Caused by bypassing municipal sewage treatment plants—4.
5. Caused by treatment of water supply reservoirs to control algae—2.
6. Caused by deliberate use of chemicals to destroy and salvage fish—5.
7. Cause unknown or questionable—26.

In those cases where the kills were caused by continuous discharges of industrial or municipal wastes, action has been completed or initiated to require the installation of adequate treatment facilities. Those caused by spills and bypassing present more difficult prevention problems.

LEGAL, ADMINISTRATIVE, AND TECHNICAL CONTROLS

The first water pollution control law dates back to before the turn of the century. Section 732.3 of the Iowa Code prohibits the throwing of dead animals, night soil, or garbage into any stream or onto adjoining land subject to overflow. The term "night soil" dates the enactment of this law, but it is still valid today in that it applies to pit privy, septic tank, and cesspool cleaners who may find a stream or adjoining land a convenient place for disposal of these wastes. Objectionable as that may be, the important violation of this law, at least in principle, is the dumping of garbage and rubbish on lands subject to overflow where above-normal stream stages wash the material downstream onto other adjoining lands. Legal counsel has advised that application of this law to municipally owned and operated dump grounds is questionable.

Today people have more time for recreational activities, and credit buying power has introduced them to the pleasure of power boating, etc. This directs attention to another source of pollution, or at least contamination, of our surface water supplies—the larger watercraft having on-board toilet and other waste disposal facilities. Some of the people demanding pollution control actually are contributors to the problem. Certainly the practice of discharging wastes with pollution propensities from watercraft, whether such craft are used for pleasure or commercial purposes, should not be condoned. This applies particularly to waters in recreational areas or near water supply intakes where hazards to the public health may be created.

Recent amendments to the Iowa Stream and Lake Pollution Law, first enacted in 1924, have already been mentioned. Two important ones are those that create a Water Pollution Control Commission and grant authority to this commission to adopt water quality and waste-water effluent standards. Creation of the commission should elevate the stature of the water pollution control program by bringing into the administration the various state agencies and other representatives of the public who are concerned not only with pollution control but also with an improvement of the quality of our surface and groundwaters. Judging from the activities of the commission thus far, the members are vigorously approaching equitable solutions for the problems that have been and will be presented to them.

In regard to administrative and technical control the former law did not prohibit per se the discharge of municipal sewage or industrial wastes into any stream or watercourse except into state-owned lakes— nor does the present law. It did and does, however, require permits for disposal of sewage and wastes, and it has been the policy of the department to require sufficient treatment to protect downstream uses. Excepted are systems receiving only domestic sewage from buildings or housing occupied by fifteen persons or less. Such systems are under the jurisdiction of the local board of health acting in line of duty of enforcing the rules and regulations of the state Department of Health which require satisfactory methods of disposal.

Insofar as degree of treatment is concerned, the department is signatory to agreements with the water pollution control agencies of Illinois and Wisconsin concerning the Mississippi River and tributaries and with the five state agencies in the lower reach of the Missouri River, both of which permit a minimum of primary treatment (removal of settleable and floatable solids) for municipal sewage and comparable industrial wastes unless additional treatment is necessary to protect downstream uses. Removal or reduction of toxic substances and other pollutants is also required. The purpose of these agreements was to control pollution of these two interstate rivers and at the same time to provide a uniform basis for protection and promotion of the econo-mies of the signatory states. These objectives have been applied to the inland waters of the state as well.

ENFORCEMENT OF WATER QUALITY STANDARDS

Thus, the idea of adopting water quality standards is not new. But heretofore the authority for their adoption has been limited to the design of new wastewater treatment facilities and the enlargement or replacement of existing facilities, whereas the newly enacted legisla-tion provides for the adoption of standards for control of existing facili-ties as well. It is hoped these standards will be used in requiring addi-tional treatment of municipal and industrial wastes where necessary to improve the quality of the receiving waters. But do not lose sight of the fact that enforcement of the new legislation will require an increased quantity and quality of personnel. The lack of such personnel has been the main obstacle in enforcing the basic provisions of the old law and this will continue to be so in enforcement of the new law. In the past the staff employed by the state Department of Health in the water pollution control program has been between six and ten qualified sanitary engineers and other subordinate employees. A recent study of the Iowa law and program, by the U.S. Public Health Service, concluded that a total of forty-three employees was advisable for adequate enforcement and administrative procedures. If the people of Iowa want abatement and control of water pollution, they must be willing to pay the costs of supporting an adequate staff of scientific and other personnel to administer the program. Police power is not enough. The program must also include qualified personnel in the field and laboratory for successful enforcement and administration.

SUMMARY

The following points summarize the Iowa situation:

1. There is a distinct need for establishing water quality and wastewater effluent standards to protect downstream uses commensurate with the economy of the state and its people.

2. Research must be advanced to find more economical and practicable methods of sewage and waste treatment. If the quality of our waters is to be improved, the costs of treatment will be high with the processes now in use.

3. There must be control of intermittent spills resulting from accidental, careless, or intentional operation of municipal sewage and industrial waste disposal facilities.

4. County and municipal officials should not permit direct connections, for the purpose of conveying sewage or industrial wastes, to drain lines installed under the drainage district laws.

5. Section 732.3, Code of Iowa, should be amended to prohibit the dumping of garbage and rubbish into streams or onto adjoining lands subject to overflow but should permit the installation of properly maintained and operated sanitary landfills on the lands subject to overflow.

6. Legislation should be enacted to control the discharge of sewage and wastes from watercraft into the interstate and inland waters of the state.

7. For ultimate improvement in surface water quality methods must be practicable for preventing pollution resulting from overflow of combined sewers.

8. Consideration should be given to the practicability of constructing storage reservoirs on Iowa streams to provide a source of dilution water during periods of low flow for sewage and wastes treated to a feasible degree.

9. Consideration should be given to enacting legislation to prevent improper construction of nonpublic water supply wells, particularly those to be used as a source for human consumption or food processing.

10. Local boards of health should be adequately staffed to regulate the installation of sewage and waste disposal facilities affecting the health and comfortable use of property within their jurisdiction.

11. Adequate educational courses should be provided to operators of public water supplies and wastewater treatment plants to enable them to become certified as competent in compliance with rigid requirements of the Operators Certification Law. The state educational institutions should continue to provide the leadership in the conduct of these courses.

12. Consideration should be given to enactment of legislation to provide financial aid for the construction and improvement of industrial waste treatment facilities with separate outlets.

PART 3
PROBLEM IDENTIFICATION AND ANALYSIS BY MAJOR WATER USERS

lear, rippling water:
:freshing to the senses,
eaceful, a source of
leasure and wealth.

CHAPTER 8

THE VIEWPOINT OF MUNICIPALITIES

JOHN R. MALONEY

IN THE EARLY DAYS OF IOWA THE NATURAL PURIFICATION ABILITY OF the streams was sufficient to care for the small amount of pollution introduced. This is no longer true due to the population growth coupled with a shift of population to the urban areas. Since 1890 the population of Iowa has increased from 1,912,297 to 2,757,537 in 1960. This has been accompanied by a shift from a 78.8 per cent rural population in 1890 to a 47.0 per cent rural population in 1960. One source has made a population projection of 3,266,000 for the year 1976; 4,514,000 for the year 2000. This forecasts an increase of 38.2 per cent by the year 2000 with respect to the 1960 census.

For many years in the water works industry it has been noted that when a city doubled its population, the water consumption was tripled. Now, with the increased per capita consumption of water, the doubling of a population indicates nearly a fourfold increase in water use. This will result in an increasing pollution load on our Iowa streams unless pollution is abated. As yet, acute problems are relatively localized on areas of the Iowa-Cedar River Basin and the Floyd-Big Sioux River Basin.

For many years the primary industry of Iowa has been agriculture. Good soil conservation practices have greatly diminished the pollution created by soil erosion. Since World War II many new industries have been established in the state. With this industrial expansion continuing, three objectives should be established:

JOHN R. MALONEY is chief chemist, Des Moines Water Works, Des Moines, Iowa.

1. Eliminate any objectionable pollution now existent by suitable construction.
2. Adopt and enforce regulations for the prevention of pollution.
3. Educate the public as to the need for pollution control.

We have long had knowledge of the hazards of pollution. Results have been published of uncontrolled pollution in many of the eastern streams, where such conditions have been reached that satisfactory solution is extremely difficult and expensive. In contrast, at present Iowa's problem is of rather limited scope and can be solved by proper treatment of wastes at the source.

WATER AND MUNICIPAL GROWTH

The growth of an urban area in our present economy is dictated by industrial development. Industrial facilities desire an assured, adequate water supply of ample quantity and of such quality that it is suitable, or can be treated economically, for the particular requirement. The schedule of water rates is in close relationship to the adequacy of the supply, insofar as community growth is concerned. A fair rate is one which is compatible with economical utility management but would encourage reuse of the water to the greatest extent practicable.

In some industries which are seasonal in nature perhaps there should be sharing, in some manner, of the cost of facilities required for their seasonal operation; for example, by a demand charge for the standby costs of large mains and storage and pumping facilities required for such intermittent use. The influence of one seasonal industry is shown dramatically in the case of Ellsworth, Iowa, which has a population of 500 according to the 1960 census. Located here is an industry which processes over a million turkeys per year. In 1961 nearly 84 per cent of the city water supply was used during the seven months when turkey processing was at a maximum.

The devising of a suitable rate schedule is far more complex than it would first appear. Almost without exception communities should engage the services of a consultant who is expert in this area when an initial rate schedule is to be established or when the existing schedule needs to be revised. Needless to say, all municipal supplies should be metered at every point of use to insure judicious use of water. In unmetered supplies the per capita use is usually very high and sizable leaks in the distribution system can go undetected for long periods. Two very good examples follow:

1. Colfax, Iowa, with a population of 2,331 (1960) has an unmetered system. The per capita water use was 152 gallons

per day compared with an average Iowa domestic use of 65 gallons per day. Des Moines, including all industrial consumption, uses approximately 114 gallons per capita daily.

2. New York City is much concerned with the lack of metering at the present time. Plans are now being made to institute the metering of all city-owned installations and to request certain other institutions to install metering on a voluntary basis. This is reported to be only for the purpose of determining consumption of these large unmetered users. The mayor of New York is also requesting a study of the rate structure and the submission of the results of the study to the Board of Estimate for their consideration.

The northeastern section of the United States has discovered that its problem has not been entirely caused from a lack of rainfall but has been due to neglect and, in some cases, mismanagement of their water resources. This situation has demonstrated that no area, regardless of its size, can afford to await the day of reckoning before taking action to ensure an adequate water supply and prevent the pollution of streams. Municipalities should encourage all methods of water conservation by consumers. In particular, water reuse by large consumers should be encouraged to the greatest possible extent consistent with economy.

RELATIONSHIP OF WATER QUALITY TO HUMAN HEALTH AND DOMESTIC USE

Man has long known of the relationship between water and certain diseases. With the use of chlorination, coagulation, sedimentation, and filtration waterborne disease has become quite rare in the developed countries of the world. This is particularly true in Iowa. Generally speaking, all municipal supplies in Iowa are satisfactory, although approximately only 45 per cent are approved by the Iowa State Department of Health. Withholding of approval is due in nearly every case to physical location of wells with respect to contaminated areas or to various undesirable factors in plant construction. These plants, of course, should improve their situation as finances permit and thus better serve their consumers.

The prime purpose of a municipal supply is the furnishing of a water to the consumers which is safe without question and is in adequate quantity. Beyond these criteria many plants find it advisable to improve the physical and/or chemical qualities of a water by suitable treatment. As the water quality of a municipal supply improves, the community will tend to become more attractive to the location of industry and thereby population growth will be stimulated.

It is technically possible to produce a safe water from highly polluted sources, even sewage. However, cost of treatment increases greatly as the pollution load increases. In some of the Iowa streams this pollution load has increased certain types of biological growth which have resulted in extreme taste and odor problems. Cedar Rapids had such an experience in 1961, and as a result it was recommended that three upstream cities proceed at once to improve their sewage treatment plants. We have in Iowa a number of industrial plants which use holding tanks for a variety of purposes, and over the years these tanks have spilled into streams. At low stream flow such spills could seriously jeopardize the operation of downstream water plants depending on the stream for their water supply. Such installations should continue to be rigorously inspected and modified, where necessary, to prevent future hazardous spills.

Of major concern are the increased hazards from materials which may be leached from soils and may enter groundwaters or surface waters. The great variety of organic herbicides, insecticides, and fungicides presents a potentially serious problem, both from the possible hazard of water contamination and because of the sophisticated laboratory procedures required for quantitative determination. Some of these materials are very stable, remaining on the soil for long periods, while others degrade to less toxic substances in a short time. Agriculture needs effective methods for the control of weeds, insects, and fungi for economical crop production and, hopefully, suitable materials which degrade rapidly can be developed. Perhaps such toxic materials could be used more judiciously or other procedures such as flame techniques could be developed. Another area of concern is the increased nitrate concentration which has been increasing during the past several years in Iowa streams and underground water supplies. Although insufficient research has been done in this area, it seems evident that this higher concentration of the nitrate ion is due to the increased use of nitrogen fertilizer. Though the answer is not immediately apparent, this would appear to be an area where the agriculturist and the sanitary engineer should cooperate in seeking a satisfactory solution.

Technology is now available for the production of a bacterially safe water and the removal of some objectionable materials and ions. However, the removal or reduction in concentration of the chloride, nitrate, sulfate, fluoride, and sodium ions from a community supply is not economically feasible. The nitrate and fluoride concentration are above recommended limits in many wells in Iowa, and economical means of reducing the concentration of these ions would greatly increase the available quantity of acceptable quality water. Research for new treatment procedures is needed in this area since use of existing ion exchange techniques for this purpose is far too costly for municipal treatment plants.

Even with the best possible sewage treatment appreciable quantities of dissolved solids are in the effluent. With adequate dilution by the stream this increase of total dissolved solids is not particularly troublesome to downstream water supplies, providing nutrients such as phosphates and nitrates are kept at reasonably low levels. These ions tend to stimulate biological growth with the attendant development of taste and odor problems. In addition, consideration of the thermal pollution problem should not be overlooked in Iowa since industrial plants will, in many cases, use streams for cooling water. It is entirely possible that this could cause Iowa streams, with their small flows much of the year, to have greater biological growths and higher temperatures than desirable for communities downstream.

In addition to treating the normal products of pollution, an abatement program must be prepared to prevent contamination from radioactive products. Industry is now using such materials in increasing quantities for a multitude of purposes and the construction of nuclear reactors also contributes to the potential problem. Although these materials must be handled under regulations of the Atomic Energy Commission, we believe their use should also be supervised by the state of Iowa. Such a program would mean adequate control of radioactive materials and prevention of excess contamination of our streams or groundwaters.

A considerable amount of data has been accumulated by the Iowa State Department of Health on the radioactive level of the streams in Iowa. As industry moves into Iowa and the use of radioactive materials becomes more widespread, this information will be invaluable. These data coupled with the mineral and sanitary analyses which have been compiled are a valuable source of information from which to establish a workable program for the abatement of pollution, both from radioactive and other sources.

Consideration must be given also to pollution of our underground water sources as well as to pollution of our streams. Frequently, an attempt is made by industry and by individuals to discharge wastewater into abandoned wells or deep seepage pits. This manner of wastewater disposal should not be permitted except in very unusual circumstances where it can be established that contamination will not occur.

After safeguarding our water supplies against pollution, we must ensure the adequacy of the supply not only for the present but for the foreseeable future. In both the area of water supply and wastewater disposal all municipalities should, by predicting their growth in a rational manner, plan ahead and have water supply and wastewater disposal facilities in existence as required by an increasing population. The municipal water plants can then produce safe, palatable water economically for the forecasted period.

ADEQUACY OF CURRENT WATER SUPPLIES

In Iowa approximately 85 per cent of the water supplies for domestic consumers is taken from wells. The glacial drift, alluvium, consolidated rock strata, and the Jordan sandstone each carry large quantities of water. The Jordan sandstone which underlies a great portion of Iowa has been estimated as containing one to two trillion gallons of water and generally is a satisfactory source. However, in some areas the fluoride concentration exceeds advisable limits. In southern Iowa, particularly, water from well supplies is inadequate. It is fortunate that in much of this area suitable reservoir construction sites can be developed.

Approximately 15 per cent of Iowa citizenry consume water produced from streams. As communities grow, this percentage will slowly increase as some of the urban areas will be forced to at least augment their supplies from Iowa streams. Most Iowa streams furnish water which can be treated to produce a water of satisfactory quality. As Iowa grows in population, pollution from all sources must be kept at a minimum for the production of satisfactory water and to keep the streams suitable for other requirements of public use.

Due to the nature of Iowa streams and the normal precipitation pattern, the quantity of water available is extremely variable. Of the average annual rainfall of 31.52 inches, approximately 6 inches is available as runoff. The remaining 25.5 inches is lost by percolation, transpiration, and evaporation. Seventy per cent of the runoff available for streams occurs between April and October. The situation is most severe during the winter months when streams are frozen and flow is at a minimum. At low flows pollution loads will decrease the quantity of dissolved oxygen. This is particularly true when the stream is frozen, making the relatively small quantity of water extremely difficult to convert into high quality water for public consumption. Iowa stream flow is highly variable. A severe flood may occur and yet in only a few weeks the stream will be at a low water level. For this reason municipalities will need to depend to an increasingly greater extent on impounded water, a method already adopted in some areas of southern Iowa.

With proper management of our water resources there should be an adequate supply of water in Iowa for the foreseeable future. This does not mean water which is readily available for all. It means that:

1. Many will need to seek water at greater depths and impoundments of surface supplies will be needed.
2. Some communities will need to use surface water as a source
   instead of wells.
3. To industry it will mean reuse of water to the greatest practicable extent.
4. Soil conservation methods will need improvement.
5. The cooperation of numerous agencies and people of various
   disciplines will be necessary in the development of a
   comprehensive water resources plan, implementation of
   which will be required to maintain an abundant supply
   of water.

ADEQUACY OF CURRENT WASTE TREATMENT AND WASTE DISPOSAL

Municipalities and industry want the highest quality water possible in the streams approaching their installation and yet in the past
have done as little as possible in the treatment of wastewater for
discharge back into the stream.

Planning for projected use by water plants, in many cases, is for
twenty-five years in the future. Nevertheless, it is the normal practice
to wait until a wastewater treatment plant is grossly overloaded before
consideration is given to enlarging the plant. The reason for this
appears to be that the average citizen has been educated to expect an
abundant supply of good quality water but he has not been educated to
the community's responsibility for wastewater treatment. Such education would appear to be of paramount importance. Until the general
public can be informed and interested in this subject, purification of
municipal wastewater will lag. Thus, the first requirement of a pollution abatement program is education of the public concerning the need.
Pride in clean streams will follow. The public has been made aware
of the national aspects of the pollution problem by all the media of
mass communication. It would appear wise to localize this education
to the requirements in Iowa.

The next steps in the abatement of pollution, following education
of the public, are the engineering and operation of the wastewater
treatment plant. The design of a wastewater treatment plant suitable
for the solution of the problem at hand is not a simple matter. The
problem may be quite complex, since we are concerned with a great
variety of waste including sanitary sewage and industrial and agricultural wastes. Among factors which must be considered are temperature; turbidity; stream turbulence and velocity; minimum stream
flow; and particularly the physical, chemical, and potential biological
characteristics of the discharge. Streams have limits as to the quantity

of pollution they can handle. These limits are a function of many variables, including the stream turbulence and time to the next point of intake. The designs for treatment plants handling domestic sewage are quite well established. Wastewater treatment plants for industrial users must be individually designed for each type of industry. Some of these plants demand sophisticated treatment with careful, capable control. For example, the Maytag plant at Newton treats a toxic waste containing cyanides, hexavalent chromium, and other products of the plating process. Through proper treatment as much as 70 per cent of their wastewater may be reused.

Two other examples outside Iowa are often cited:

1. Bethlehem Steel Co., Sparrowpoint, Md., reduced pumpage of groundwater by 80 per cent by purchasing, coagulating, and reusing over 40 million gallons daily of treated Baltimore sewage effluent.
2. Celanese Corporation's plant, Bishop, Texas, recirculates cooling water fifty times before discharge and by this procedure has reduced its water requirements from 230 to 4 million gallons daily.

The range of costs of water reuse in the United States are:

1. Industrial water from a municipal supply costs 2–25 cents per 1,000 gallons.
2. Recycled cooling water costs 1–5 cents per 1,000 gallons.
3. Treated sewage effluent costs 2–13 cents per 1,000 gallons.

This would indicate that reuse of water and/or the purchase of treated sewage effluent with the necessary treatment for use as process water is an ecomical procedure for large plants and possibly for some small plants, depending on their requirements.

TRENDS IN DEVELOPMENT AND CONSTRUCTION

Water Supplies

Well supplies in Iowa tend to produce hard waters, high in iron and hydrogen sulfide. Surface waters are characterized by a fairly high average hardness and during much of the year carry fairly high threshold odors. With the rising standard of living, particularly since World War II, consumers are no longer content to endure these undesirable characteristics in water which they consume, even though it is established to be bacterially safe. To meet the increased demand, communities are, as their finances permit, installing treatment facilities to produce a more acceptable water and increasing the quantity of water available.

The Housing and Urban Development Act of 1965 makes grants available to water utilities for "basic public water facilities, including works for the storage, treatment, purification, and the distribution of water." These grants may be up to 50 per cent of the cost of the project and no limitation on the size of the utility or project is fixed by the law. Some installations may require complex treatment while some may only require chlorination and, in the case of surface supplies, lime-soda softening is often employed. New installations usually are designed for control of tastes and odors by appropriate treatment.

Abatement of pollution in Iowa streams will render the production of a satisfactory water much more certain. The demand for high quality water by consumers has made and is making the operation of a water plant more technical in nature, which dictates a higher level of abilities for the operators. This was recognized in 1958 by the Iowa Section of the American Water Works Association with the institution of a voluntary certification program. The 1964–65 legislature, recognizing the need, passed laws making it mandatory for all water plants to employ a certified operator after July 4, 1966. With training courses available and with proper administration of this program, the modernized plants will have capable operation.

Waste Disposal Facilities

There are 944 municipalities in Iowa, 465 having sanitary sewers and 424 having sewage treatment plants. All cities of over 15,000 population have treatment facilities. Thus, over 90 per cent of the population of municipalities are served by sewage treatment plants. These plants, very generally speaking, are adequate, although some are overloaded and others are not operated at their maximum efficiency. The design of a waste treatment plant is normally based on the minimum seven-day flow of a stream for a ten-year period. In some cases when an industry moves into a community, the additional requirements appreciably overload the treatment plant. Two of the industries presenting problems are the meat packing plants and the anhydrous ammonia producers. Gravel and stone washing operations also often cause objectionably high turbidities. In the northern part of Iowa the streams begin with very small flows in most cases. This must be considered in controlling the amount of contamination which may be permitted to enter these streams.

Approximately twenty-five extended aeration plants have been constructed in Iowa, primarily by private industry. However, most Iowa wastewater treatment plants are of trickling filter design. In recent years the use of waste stabilization ponds has become quite common, particularly for the smaller municipalities, schools, and private enterprises. There are 143 of these ponds operating and it is probable that this type of installation will find increasing favor in the smaller communities where waste treatment does not exist.

Waste treatment in Iowa has progressed from a position of slightly over 300,000 persons served by municipal waste treatment in 1920 to the 1,730,028 served in the midsixties. This progress is certainly of interest and satisfaction to those who process water for human consumption. With the increase in population and industry, wastewater treatment needs careful control and skilled operation if we desire to prevent pollution of our streams. As in the case of water treatment it is hoped that the requirement for plants to operate under the supervision of certified operators will improve the efficiency of wastewater treatment plants.

The Sixty-first General Assembly of Iowa passed the Iowa Stream and Pollution Law which was effective July 4, 1965. Thus, the third requirement for pollution control is available—enforcement. This is a necessary adjunct to education and engineering. It is easy to lay all pollution problems at the door of industry. We believe that industry will do its part if the individual communities also set the example by good wastewater treatment. It certainly is not fair to require industrial users to treat their wastewater to a higher degree than does the community of which they are a part.

EXISTING OR ANTICIPATED PROBLEMS

The most difficult problem appears to be the cost of improvements for water and wastewater treatment plants. Even though federal funds are available, the community must bear some of the cost and such plants are paid for indirectly by the taxpayer. Presenting not insurmountable problems are the various viewpoints of the several disciplines of engineering, science, law, agriculture, industry, conservation, and perhaps other groups who have specialized interest in a program which affects streams. These can and must all be reconciled and the Iowa State Comprehensive Water Plan now in development is the first step in this direction.

The low stream flows in the northern portion of the state have been mentioned. How much pollution can be permitted to enter these low-flow streams, particularly when they are ice covered, and be made harmless by self-purification of the stream and by dilution by other tributaries? Will industrial development of this area of the state be held to only those industries which will not pollute the streams? In a particular case, can an industry treat its wastewater to a sufficiently high level? Perhaps holding ponds of sufficient capacity would be a satisfactory solution in some cases.

Pollution has been represented as a finite material which could be detected with a positive prediction of the results when it was introduced into a stream. Unfortunately, this is not true and those familiar with the subject realize that numerous gaps exist in our knowledge in this area. For example:

1. Synergistic and antagonistic effects of pollutants.
2. Rates of decomposition of pollutants under various conditions.
3. Flow characteristics of pollutants in various stream flows.
4. Allowable concentrations for the many, literally thousands, of new organic chemicals which may be discharged into streams.
5. Limitation of data available on streams due to infrequency of sampling.
6. Variation of concentration of contaminant entering the stream.
7. Long-term effects on biological life, and on man, of some of the unfamiliar chemicals which may enter our streams.

Congress in 1965 passed legislation which set up the Water Pollution Control Administration. This act toughens the federal role in pollution abatement considerably. States and cities are required to establish water quality criteria and plans for their implementation by June 30, 1967, and grants for the construction of sewage treatment plants are liberalized under this act. It appears strongly advisable for the respective states and the larger cities to develop suitable standards for the control of pollution and to proceed to implement these standards rather than waiting for the federal government to do so. This will serve a dual purpose in that pollution abatement will proceed more rapidly and the respective states can set more effective standards for themselves than those which may be set by a federal agency. The longer such action is delayed, the greater will be the cost.

With the setting of a satisfactory standard for the quality of wastewater; the education of the public as to the need, competent engineering, and operation of wastewater treatment plants; and the enforcement of existing regulation, the streams of Iowa can be brought to and maintained at satisfactory levels of quality for the provision of ample quantity and quality of water for the citizens of Iowa. Our water resources must be managed for the maximum benefit of society.

DISCUSSION

HARRIS F. SEIDEL

JOHN R. MALONEY HAS PRESENTED AN EXCELLENT REVIEW OF THE current domestic water supply and pollution control situation in Iowa. It is an interesting and perceptive look at our past and present and includes some thoughtful projections into the future. He has highlighted three objectives or needs for successful water pollution control in Iowa. These are as follows: (1) engineering, (2) education, and (3) enforcement. These points are well taken. This discussion is intended to emphasize further these three points then to suggest a fourth which is equally, if not more, important.

ENGINEERING

It is worth repeating that 424 municipalities in Iowa in 1965 were served by waste treatment plants. This includes 91 per cent of the total urban population in Iowa and 97 per cent of the population with sanitary sewers. By far the majority of towns with neither sewers nor waste treatment are under 500 population. Iowa presently has only isolated acute pollution problems. A related factor is that only 15 per cent of our cities now use streams as a source of water supply. The interrelationship between these factors is a fortunate circumstance.

On the one hand Iowa can boast of a substantial record of achievement in water pollution control contrasted to other states which have embarked on major construction programs only in the last several years. For example, over 200 waste treatment plants had been built in Iowa by 1925.

On the other hand Maloney also points out that much of our planning in waste treatment has been too little and too late and that often wastes are treated as little as possible before discharge back to the stream. We must generally plead guilty to this accusation as well.

EDUCATION

Our defense for some of what we have not done has been the claim that there was little or no public support for effective water pollution control. Waste treatment has been considered the proper thing to do, but the price has seemed too high. All this has changed rather dramatically in the last several years. We are now confronted

HARRIS F. SEIDEL is director, Water and Pollution Control, City of Ames, Iowa.

with feature articles and displays in national magazines, coupled with emotional and colorful statements by "authorities" in many walks of life, which are intended to convince anyone in doubt that a major national heritage is quickly slipping down the drain. Some of these analyses are carefully done and responsibly phrased. Others are less than objective and rational.

We have almost become accustomed to being told that our rivers are "open sewers," and that pollution is "like a cancer that is silently spreading deadly cells to vital organs." A case in point is Sioux City whose pollution problems continue to be publicized even several years after its plant for treatment of municipal and meat packing wastes has been completed and placed in service.

It is truly unfortunate that equal space is not given to institutions such as the Ohio River Sanitation Commission under whose auspices the Ohio River has been transformed from one of our most polluted streams to a healthy artery about which there has been little or no publicity in years. Another example is the Missouri River. Ten years ago no major city on the Missouri had a waste treatment plant; today no major city on the Missouri is without a treatment plant either completed or under construction. This is real progress, but not the type of story to rate headlines.

ENFORCEMENT

Enforcement is a matter of both law and attitude. It is quite apparent that both are rapidly becoming much more rigorous with regard to pollution control. In 1956 Public Law 660 provided construction grants-in-aid for water pollution control in the amount of $50 million per year. It also provided support for research and similar elements of a national attack on water pollution. The funds available for such grants have since been increased to the level of $150 million per year, and additional funds have been appropriated for research and development and for studies of the problem of storm water separation and treatment.

The 1965 Water Quality Act provides that the water pollution control effort be removed from the U.S. Public Health Service and placed under a separate administration within the department of Health, Education, and Welfare. Another major provision is that the states are expected to establish water quality standards by mid-1967, failing which the federal government will do this job for them.

Whether we particularly approve of these provisions or not, we must recognize that they represent the weight of current public opinion. In its final form the Muskie bill was passed in the U.S. Senate by a vote of something like 65 to 9, and the Blatnik bill was passed in the House by a vote of 395 to 0. Following conference agreement on certain sections of these two measures, the final bill was passed unanimously in both houses of Congress.

We must also recognize that current legislation is probably not the last word in this area. In signing the 1965 act into law on October 2, President Johnson stated:

> This moment marks a very proud beginning for the United States of America. Today, we proclaim our refusal to be strangled by the wastes of civilization. Today, we begin to be masters of our environment.
> But we must act, and act swiftly. The hour is late, the damage is large.
>
>   o   o   o   o   o
>
> I believe that with your help and your continued cooperation, water pollution is doomed in this century.
> This bill that you have passed, that will become law as a result of a responsive Congress, will not completely assure us of absolute success. Additional bolder legislation will be needed in the years ahead. But we have begun. And we have begun in the best American tradition—with a program of joint Federal, State, and local action.
>
>   o   o   o   o   o

OPERATION

In addition to the engineering, education, and enforcement stressed by Maloney, it is essential that we focus attention on the need for competent operation.

A Neglected Department

Traditionally, many cities forced to build waste treatment plants have not been overly concerned about their proper operation. All too often the operator of a generation ago was selected for that position either because he was at or beyond retirement age and no pension plan was available or he was a misfit or troublemaker who seemed unable to fit anywhere else in the city organization. His pay was low, the budget for maintenance and repairs was pitifully small, and the operator was usually untrained and unconcerned about it.

Does this appear to be an overdrawn picture of an illegitimate department run by a second-class citizen? Many with long experience in this field will recognize that it is quite faithful to the truth in far too many cases. One of the most naive but still one of the most long-lived notions in this field of pollution control has been that if a waste treatment plant were built, it would then in some rather remarkable way proceed to do its job with little or no further attention.

During Senate hearings on the Muskie bill, the Water Pollution Control Federation submitted a prepared statement which included this sentence: "It is this organization's experience that the provision of adequate operation is the greatest single problem in water pollution control."

A Voice From the Past

A paper presented by a staff engineer of the Iowa State Department of Health to an early meeting of waste treatment operators and other officials contains some interesting comments. It was based on a survey of fifty-seven Iowa plants which indicated that more than half were "in very bad shape due to a lack of proper attention." The following excerpt will give some clues to the date of the survey:

> Some of the troubles reported in connection with the sand beds were growth of weeds, deep plowing with horse power, replacement of filter sand with a dirty non-uniform pit run sand, overloading as a result of a high rate of infiltration into the sewers, and failure to repair the distribution system. Some of the filter beds were by-passed entirely, because the siphons were out of order.

It is interesting that in certain respects the situation today is not radically improved over that next described:

> There are two reasons why there are so many poorly operated municipal sewage-treatment plants in Iowa. The first reason is that the average city or town council fails to realize the necessity of providing a competent, intelligent and industrious plant operator to perform certain fundamental duties at the right time and in the right way; and the second reason is that the average council fails to provide yearly a sufficient repair and replacement fund.

What suggestions did that early observer have for righting this wrong? He concluded his paper with these three:

> (1) Licensed operators. It is proposed that a state law be passed requiring every city or town having a municipal sewage-treatment plant to employ a licensed operator to look after the plant.
>
> (2) Weekly reports. It is proposed that each operator be required to fill in a weekly report card as furnished by the State Department of Health.
>
> (3) Inspection engineer. It is proposed that a full-time sanitary engineer be added to the Sanitary Engineering Division of the State Department of Health, whose duty it will be to visit each municipal sewage-treatment plant in the state periodically for the purpose of investigating the plant and advising both the council and the operator concerning things that should be done to improve the operation.

A final quotation from that paper is the following gem:

> If it is necessary to install sewage-treatment plants in the first place, it is certainly necessary that they function properly; and the best way to assure good operation is to provide competent men to look after them.

That paper was given by Hans Pedersen at a meeting in Ames in November, 1925, exactly forty years from the date of this conference. (See Hans V. Pedersen, "Better Operation for Iowa Sewage-Treatment Plants," Iowa State College Eng. Ext. Bul. 80, Vol. 24, No. 37, Feb. 10, 1926.) In the intervening years we have learned to orbit astronauts and to fire projectiles at the moon. Clearly, our progress in pollution control has not kept pace.

Hopefully, Hans can draw some satisfaction from the passage early in 1965 of an operator licensing or certification law covering both water and pollution control personnel. With respect to the reports he recommended, few are being submitted and little attention is paid to those which are received. Because of the press of other duties such as inspection of trailer parks, nursing homes, and swimming pools, the present field staff of the state Department of Health has little time for visits to water and pollution control plants except on an emergency or troubleshooting basis.

What Is Operation?

In general terms waste treatment might be considered a production process; the raw material consists of various solids suspended and dissolved in water, and the end product consists of water again, along with by-product solids and a combustible gas.

Disregarding for a moment all the social, political, and emotional factors which currently exert such great influence, this production process might well be approached in the following business-like manner:

1. Set certain standards or goals for the process in terms of removal efficiency, quality of effluent, or similar criteria.
2. Secure competent personnel to manage and operate the "enterprise" and support them with an adequate operating budget.
3. Establish a system of analyses, records, and reports to maintain control of and evaluate the efficiency or success of the process.

If the above approach has any validity, why should it not be applied to the waste treatment field? One or more of the above criteria are completely lacking in the management of most waste treatment plants in Iowa and other states as well. In fact, many plants are operated in an incredibly careless manner. This is worse than irresponsible nonsense. *This is fraud!*

Let us take Ames as an example. The city and Iowa State University are served by a water pollution control plant completed in 1950 at a cost of $1 million. Operating costs of approximately $90,000 per year are shared by the partners in this joint venture. Add to this a rough figure of $60,000 for annual fixed charges, and the total cost to the Ames community for waste treatment becomes, in round numbers, $150,000 per year.

For this annual expenditure of $150,000 what are the people of Ames receiving in return? Hopefully, they are receiving a sufficiently competent job of waste treatment plant operation so that the Skunk River can always be considered one of Iowa's clean streams. Is this objective in fact being met? What treatment results are being achieved? Who really knows? (It might even be relevant to ask: Who cares?)

Every waste treatment plant should be striving toward some specific standards and it should be obligated to report regularly on its performance. Failing in either of these, things should begin to happen to those in responsible charge of the plant.

Condition of the Receiving Stream

The lack of interest or emphasis on the quality of the receiving stream as a goal of waste treatment is quite surprising. The plant operator who does any sampling whatever of the stream below his plant outfall is rare indeed. Yet the receiving stream must be considered a vital link in the overall water resources cycle, and its condition should be high on the list of routine operating data. What are the conditions in our Iowa streams today? We must admit that our store of knowledge in this area is sparse indeed, but we must also recognize that this is another result of the minimal financial support our state Department of Health has received over the years.

CONCLUSION

The first objective stressed by Maloney was that of *engineering* under which we might also include planning and development. This is a major objective but one which is currently being met by a very aggressive effort in waste treatment research, process development, and production of improved materials and equipment. The real lag here is in translating these advances into practice.

The second objective stressed was that of *education*. It is agreed that this is an area of real concern; but through the efforts of such media as The Reader's Digest and various Sunday supplements, this objective is being met, even though we may not appreciate the harum-scarum methods often used.

The third objective cited by Maloney was *enforcement*. An enforcement program first involves some judgment as to the standards and criteria which are to be enforced, then the development and training of a staff to do the job. In Chapter 8 Paul Houser focuses the harsh light of reality on our needs in this succinct statement:

If the people of Iowa want abatement and control of water pollution, they must be willing to pay the costs of supporting an adequate staff of scientific and other personnel to administer the program. Police power is not enough. The program must also include qualified personnel in the field and laboratory for successful enforcement and administration.

Finally, let us return to the often overlooked subject of *operation*. We have a new water pollution control law in Iowa. We also now have an operator certification or licensing law. Through the federal grant program, stricter state legislation, and the momentum of public opinion we have learned how to motivate the construction of waste treatment plants in cities large and small. The great and obvious gap remaining is that we have not yet learned how to secure operation, really competent operation, of these facilities. Certainly this is one of the elements of enforcement.

We have been concerned in the past with problem identification and analysis. Competent operation would seem to be the most serious problem; competent operation of waste treatment facilities remains the key to successful water resource management.

DISCUSSION

A. L. BENNETT

JOHN R. MALONEY HAS POINTED OUT THAT IOWA NOW HAS AN AMPLE supply of water to meet our present requirements and that the quality of this supply is such that it usually can be treated to produce a satisfactory domestic water supply. He has, however, flagged our attention to possible future shortages, both from a quantity and quality standpoint. We are faced with this problem because of the population increase in our suburban areas, the tremendous growth of industry in the state, and our possible failure to take the necessary precautions or to institute planning to prevent pollution of the waters of the state in the future.

NEED FOR PLANNING

Maloney mentions the need for planning if we are to protect and conserve our water resources. Planning is being done at the federal level as evidenced by the establishment of the Water Pollution Control

A. L. BENNETT was formerly director, Water Supply and Swimming Pool Division, Iowa State Department of Health, Des Moines, Iowa.

Division in the U.S. Department of Health, Education, and Welfare; at the state level by the recent passage of the new Iowa Stream and Lake Pollution Law; and at local levels as evidenced by the many new and remodeled waste treatment plants constructed in Iowa in the late fifties and early sixties. This planning must be continued at all levels. What can happen when planning is not adequate was illustrated by the New York City water crisis. In our department we frequently note the lack of planning or management by small-town municipal officials. As an example of poor management of a small town's water supply the monthly water samples submitted to the state Hygienic Laboratory began showing contamination present and the situation was apparently becoming serious. An engineer was sent to the community to investigate the contamination and eliminate it from the supply if possible. The town had only one drilled well. The production from this one well had been gradually decreasing over a period of several years and the water demand kept increasing until a situation developed where the one well was unable to keep up with the demand. In order to keep water in the elevated tank for fire protection purposes, the water superintendent for several hours each day was valving off the entire distribution system, pumping only into the elevated tank. With no pressure on the system, contamination was certain to gain entrance to the supply through back-siphonage, leaking mains, etc. To correct this situation, the supply was disinfected with chlorine, pressure was maintained on the system at all times even though the tank was not completely full, and the town took action toward drilling another well. But here, certainly, was an instance where the municipal officials failed their community by lack of planning. This illustrates the quality of planning or management we must expect to work with in solving some of our water pollution problems. This is also a good example of why we need better trained operators for our water and wastewater treatment plants.

WATER QUALITY AND HUMAN HEALTH

The relationship between water quality and human health has also been pointed out by Maloney. All surface waters in Iowa contain some degree of contamination, with even our lakes and protected impoundments receiving some contamination from normal runoff. All of our surface waters can presently be treated by conventional water treatment procedures to result in a finished water of satisfactory bacterial quality. Even Cedar Rapids with their taste and odor problems in 1961 still produced a water safe to drink. Several towns in northwest Iowa use lake water treated only by chlorination yet maintain an excellent bacterial record.

Our groundwaters, other than the shallow waters or those found in creviced limestone rock, are generally of a satisfactory bacterial quality. Many private wells when tested will show contamination present but this is generally due to poor location or improper construction of the well. We have had relatively few instances of contamination of municipal wells from the use of drainage wells and waste disposal wells. In principle we feel that such waste disposal practices should be discouraged because of the contamination that is added directly to groundwater aquifers. They certainly represent a potential source of contamination and should be controlled. The Iowa Natural Resources Council has followed a policy restricting the use of such wells.

Maloney also notes that our Iowa groundwater is often highly mineralized, requiring treatment for most domestic purposes. Removal of iron is commonest, 240 of our 733 public water supplies now employing this treatment. High sulfate content is common, some wells in Iowa producing a water that cannot be tolerated by humans because of the cathartic effect. Nitrates are a problem of shallow wells and, as mentioned by Maloney, a number of our public water supplies use water with amounts of nitrates above the recommended limit. However, as of 1965 we had received no report of infant cyanosis, the disease associated with high nitrates, from any of the public water supplies in question.

NEED FOR RESEARCH

The need for additional research to enable the waterworks industry to produce a finished water of satisfactory quality has been cited. The industry has made progress in this respect but there is much left to be accomplished. The waterworks profession must not be lulled into placing the blame for all its problems of taste and odors, algae blooms, turbidity, and other problems on stream pollution. They should be able to treat raw water with certain undesirable characteristics and produce a safe, palatable water. We have had problems of taste and odors in our water supplies since the beginning of waterworks history. We have algae blooms in our water supplies where no pollution exists. Problems of color, turbidity, and mineral content have always been with us and they are problems to which the waterworks industry itself must find the solution. In too many cases there is a tendency for the waterworks profession to blame a poor tasting water or one that is not entirely satisfactory on pollution from some source over which they have no control when, in fact, the failure is often that of the waterworks in not having the know-how and the tools to produce the desired water. Again, we might illustrate the case with the example of Cedar Rapids in 1961 when the taste and odor in the raw water could not be satisfactorily removed by their treatment plant. The raw water had a very high algae count, the water actually taking on the appearance of pea-green soup. This algae concentration was present in the stream all the way to its source in Minnesota so all the blame for this situation should not have been placed on the sources of pollution known to exist a short distance upstream from Cedar Rapids. The Cedar Rapids water treatment plant simply did not have the facilities or the necessary know-how to treat this algae-laden water to make it palatable. Safe, yes, but certainly not a palatable or satisfactory finished product. This illustrates the great need for research in water treatment so that we may cope with the many problems of raw-water quality which we must expect to face in Iowa. The present effort on the part of the federal government in the desalinization program is a good illustration of the type of effort needed in the research field of water treatment.

Ending with a note of optimism, Maloney's chapter points out that the pollution of our Iowa water resources is not yet acute, and with adequate planning and enforcement the waters of Iowa can be brought to and maintained at satisfactory levels of quality so as to assure an ample quantity and quality of water supply for the citizens of Iowa.

SELECTED REFERENCES

1. A. P. Black, "Challenges of Water Quality," *Jour. Amer. Water Works Assn.*, Vol. 56 (1964), p. 1279.
2. Bureau of Labor Statistics, "Projections to the Years 1976–2000, Economic Growth, Population, Labor Force and Leisure," Reports to Outdoor Recreation Resources Review Commission, Study Rept. 23 (Washington, D.C., USGPO, 1962).
3. A. K. Cherry, "Rx for Tastes and Odors," *Water Works Engineering*, Vol. 115 (1962), p. 182.
4. W. L. Gasper, "Industrial Waste Treatment, A Case History," private communication.
5. Iowa Natural Resources Council, "Inventory of Water Resources," Bul. 1–8 (State of Iowa, 1953–59).
6. Iowa State Department of Health, "Iowa Water Supply Data," (Des Moines, Iowa, Division of Public Health Engineering, 1964).
7. P. J. Jehlik and R. E. Wakely, "Rural-Urban Migration in Iowa, 1940–50," Iowa State Univ. Ag. Ext. Serv. Bul. 407, Apr., 1954.
8. F. W. Schaller and B. G. Riley, "The Water Problem in Iowa," Iowa State Univ. Ag. Ext. Serv. Bul. P-122, Jan., 1957.
9. U.S. Bureau of Census Reports (Washington, D.C., Dept. of Commerce, 1960).
10. U.S. Department of Health, Education, and Welfare, "The Living Waters" (Washington, D.C., U.S. Publ. Health Serv., 1961).
11. *Ibid.*, "The Struggle for Clean Water," 1962.
12. *Ibid.*, "Water Quality Measurement and Instrumentation" (Cincinnati, Ohio, Robert A. Taft Sanitary Engineering Center, 1961).
13. U.S. Geological Survey and Iowa Geological Survey, "Water Story in Central Iowa," Iowa Water Atlas No. 1 (State of Iowa, 1965).

CHAPTER 9

THE INDUSTRIAL POINT OF VIEW

H. SIDWELL SMITH

Iowa is in transition from agricultural to industrial economic predominance. The market value of industrial goods now exceeds that of farm products. This is not because of declining agricultural production; it is due to increasing industrial production. All evidence indicates continuance of this trend.

GENERAL CONSIDERATIONS

Some of the political, social, and economic shifts associated with Iowa's move toward industrialization are apparent to even the casual observer. However, subtler changes, some technological and some socioeconomic in nature, have occurred or will occur. These changes can affect the course of both industrial and nonindustrial development. They are, in large measure, susceptible to control. The future pattern of the state's economy can be significantly affected by the nature of these controls.

Increasing industrial use of Iowa's water resources is one of these subtle changes. Iowa's favorable situation with regard to water availability is a factor favoring expansion of existing industry and attraction of new industry. However, water disposal of industrial wastes introduces a use of our water resources which, in varying degrees, is incompatible with other industrial and nonindustrial uses.

Water use can be controlled, whether the use is for waste disposal, recreation, or other purposes. In developing such controls, however,

H. SIDWELL SMITH is professor and chairman, Department of Civil Engineering, University of Iowa, Iowa City, Iowa.

we must recognize that there are competing uses and the controls must of necessity include compromises to reconcile these conflicting interests. The wisdom with which these controls are designed can have profound influence on the future economic and social complexion of our state.

Industrial as well as municipal abuses of Iowa's water resources have been and are occurring. However, when compared with regions where intense industrial activity has been long established, Iowa is in its infancy with respect to industrial use of water resources. The design of water use policies for regions where long-entrenched abuses exist is a most difficult task. Iowa enjoys the advantage of working from a position which has a greater essence of preventive rather than corrective philosophy toward abuses of water. This advantage, however, is fleeting. Action *now* toward the formulation of workable water use policies will minimize the much more painful corrective actions. It is important that this urgency be recognized.

PRE-1960 NATURE OF INDUSTRIAL WASTE PROBLEM

Prior to about 1960 Iowa's industry, with a few notable exceptions, was concerned largely with food processing. The major industrial waste producers were meat, milk, vegetable, and grain processing industries. Wastes produced by these industries are largely organic in nature. Their effect on water resources is concerned with oxygen depletion and eutrophic phenomena rather than direct toxicity. They are amenable to biological treatment and are frequently treated in combination with municipal wastes.

There are no reliable data available on the total magnitude of these wastes. Monitoring of individual plant wastes is rare and regulatory manpower has not been available from any local, state, or federal agency to provide a definite inventory of these wastes except in specific instances where gross pollution has forced action. Information on operating industrial waste treatment installations is frequently difficult to procure. For many years the U.S. Public Health Service has collected data and published periodic inventories of waste treatment facilities. Industrial waste facilities have not been included since the 1957 inventory reportedly due to the extreme difficulty of obtaining reliable information on operational industrial treatment facilities.

Some idea of the magnitude of part of these raw wastes can be gleaned from gross production of meat and dairy products. In 1960 Iowa plants processed approximately 6 billion pounds of cattle and hogs and 250 million pounds of poultry. About 350 million pounds of butter and milk products were also produced. The oxygen required for biological stabilization of the wastes from these operations was equivalent to that required by the wastes from a population of about 4 million persons. The total population equivalent of all organic industrial wastes generated in the state in 1960 probably approximated 6 million persons or on the order of twice the total population.

Of course, Iowa's pre-1960 industrial wastes were not solely due to food processing. Machinery, appliance, and electronics manufacturing produced wastes typical of these operations. In some instances these have been responsible for serious local pollution incidents which have forced corrective action. However, these wastes when considered overall seem to have had less continuous impact on our water resources than those of an organic nature originating in our agriculture-related industries.

It is obvious that even Iowa's generous water resources cannot continuously receive raw municipal and industrial wastes from a combined population equivalent approaching 10 million persons without gross depreciation of those resources. Diffusion of industrial activity and population over a large geographic area rather than concentration in a large metropolitan center has dispersed the pollution load over a larger portion of the total water resource, thus minimizing the severity in any given region. Municipal and industrial treatment systems, either separate or combined, generally have reduced locally critical pollutional loads to a degree that, even if not completely satisfactory, has at least kept the overall pollution situation at a fairly low level of public pressure.

CHANGES SINCE 1960

Since 1960 the following trends have affected the Iowa industrial waste situation:

1. The advent of new type industries such as the chemical industry complex along the Mississippi River.
2. The continued growth of existing industry.
3. An aroused public interest in water resources, particularly pollutional aspects of water use.

The rising importance of new type industries is accompanied by new waste constituents, many of which are not amenable to treatment by conventional methods and whose effect on the receiving water is different than oxygen depletion and related phenomena customarily used as pollution indices. For example, the wastes from chemical fertilizer plants contain nitrogen and phosphates which are not removed in conventional biological treatment processes but are important algal nutrients.

Expansion of existing plants and construction of new food processing plants has been rapid. This is to be expected with movement of processing plants away from concentrated metropolitan areas toward centers of raw material production. This has been especially noticed in the meat packing industry. New construction has resulted in large centers of potential pollution in relatively small communities such as Perry, Denison, Cherokee, Columbus Junction, and Tama.

Perhaps the most significant development of 1960–65 has been gradual public realization that water is indeed a vital and valuable natural resource which can be used in various and sometimes competing ways. A direct result of this enlightened opinion is the emphasis on water pollution control. In Iowa this has led directly to the establishment of the Water Pollution Control Commission. These actions have highlighted the industrial waste problems because of the relatively great effect of industrial wastes on the total pollutional load.

Therefore, it would seem that whereas the situation in 1960 was one of only moderate deficiency with respect to conditions publicly acceptable, the early 1960's have moved Iowa into a situation where increasing industrial waste loads and more critical public requirements create a climate of rapidly diverging interests. This divergence is not yet critical but, as previously noted, it may well become so if the formulation of policies needed to reconcile differing interests is delayed so long that a large degree of corrective rather than preventive action is necessary.

The most difficult problems relating to water pollution by industrial users are concerned with water use policies. The balance of this chapter will examine some aspects of policy making.

WATER USE POLICY CONSIDERATIONS

Two general areas need to be examined in arriving at policies or guidelines for the regulation of waterborne wastes:

1. Technological questions concerned with methods of waste control at the source, methods of waste treatment, the effect of waste constituents on the receiving waters, and the assimilative capacity of the waters.
2. Political, social, and economic questions concerned with evaluation of competing uses of the water, allocation of assimilative capacity among various users, and reconciliation of differences in economic views between public and private users as these views affect determination of best use and program formulation.

Neither of these areas is independent of the other. This dependency will become apparent as this discussion continues.

Nature of Technological Problems—Water Quality Standards

The most vexing technological problems are not those concerned with source control or treatment of industrial wastes. They are, instead, concerned with the effect of waste constituents on receiving waters and the capacity of the waters to assimilate these constituents without adversely affecting other uses of the water.

This does not mean that all is known that need be known about methods of waste minimization by industrial process modification or that best methods of treatment are known for all wastes. Such will never be the case. Nevertheless the nature of these problems is such that they can be identified and defined so that intensive research effort may be brought to bear when necessary. Moreover, their solution may be a direct economic benefit to the particular industry, hence motivation for the needed research is reasonably high.

On the other hand there is relatively meager quantitative knowledge of the effects of waste constituents on receiving waters. This knowledge is necessary as a base for rational definition of water quality for given water uses or classes of receiving waters. Industry and municipalities alike must be provided with clear and unequivocal receiving water quality standards to provide a sound basis upon which to plan pollution abatement and control measures. Equivocation in this responsibility by regulatory agencies is a disservice when it fails to provide either industry or municipalities with any assurance that planning conditions agreed upon at a given time will continue to be firm.

Establishment of water quality standards must, of necessity, reflect the best possible compromise among competing uses. To this extent water quality standards are a political, social, and economic problem. However, technology must provide evaluation of the effects of each component of each use on all other uses before these socioeconomic factors can be evaluated. Moreover, technology must afford some notion of the costs involved for varying degrees of pollution abatement necessary to accommodate nonpollutional uses of water.

Special Industrial Considerations

Such matters are directly related to industry. In contrast to municipalities, industry is mobile. New industry has considerable latitude in choice of location. Existing industry has freedom of decision as to whether or not to expand in a given location. Waste control measures necessary to meet specified water quality standards are important factors in location decision. This decision, in turn, will be important in affecting the economy of the region.

Industry contributes its special flavor to the problem by the different and sometimes exotic constituents of its wastes. What is the effect on the receiving stream of a plastic-film waste which is resistant to biological degradation and hence creates but little oxygen demand, is not toxic, but completely changes the character of the stream bottom?

What are the effects of phosphates, nitrates, and similar "fertilizing" nutrients found in some chemical wastes? How serious is the secondary pollution they cause by promoting algal growth? What is the real tolerance of our streams toward such toxic items as cyanide, chromium, copper, cadmium, and arsenic compounds? What is the effect of thermal pollution? These questions relate to existing Iowa industrial waste situations and need quantitative answers before complete water quality standards can be established.

Effect of Pollution From Surface Runoff

At this point it must be made clear that the "zero tolerance" or "drinking water" concept of water quality standards is not realistic. Even if it were technically and economically feasible to remove every trace of contaminant from a municipal or industrial waste stream, the fact that all receiving waters contain pollutants from surface runoff which are difficult or impossible to control makes it totally unreasonable to go to this extreme in waste treatment except in very unusual cases. Consider the fact that natural waters even in primeval regions contain the residues of a multitude of life processes occurring on the watershed. The concentrations of these residues may be well below any levels significant to the highest order of human use but they do, nevertheless, constitute a degree of pollution which is noncontrollable. Consider now the situation of contaminants conveyed in the runoff from our urban and rural areas. These include turbidity and organic products resulting from agriculture and natural life cycles and chemical residues from various operations on the drainage area. Even if no industrial or urban pollution existed, it is inconceivable that water in the Iowa, Des Moines, or Cedar rivers would be of drinking quality without treatment. Here again the nature of this pollution is such that there is little likelihood of significant control. Sewage contained in overflow from combined storm and sanitary sewers can be controlled and is not of this class of contaminants.

The magnitude of this surface runoff pollution needs to be defined and included in consideration of water quality standards. Some notion of its possible magnitude is indicated by observations of the Iowa River above the Coralville reservoir during the course of a water quality surveillance study in progress at the University of Iowa. In January, 1965, precipitation and high runoff from frozen ground occurred over the watershed after an extended period of snow cover and no runoff. The resulting increase in biochemical oxygen demand in the river corresponded to the sewage from more than 500,000 persons. Severe oxygen depression and some fish kill occurred in the Iowa River and the Coralville flood control reservoir. Circumstances were such that there is little doubt this "slug" of pollution was due to runoff from the open land. A scheme of water quality standards which required high-degree treatment of industrial or municipal wastes while neglecting overland pollution of this degree would not be realistic. It is obvious that some better knowledge of this source of pollution is needed in order that all factors affecting water quality can be rationally considered.

Steps Toward Water Quality Standards

These thoughts concerning the technological problems surrounding establishment of water quality standards point up the need for far more qualified attention to this phase of stream pollution than has been given to date. This is a matter of concern to industries and municipalities alike. However, rapid industrial growth and the predominant role of industry in creation of potential pollution means that the present urgency for action can be laid at the doorstep of industry. The scope of the problem of water quality standards for Iowa is so large and complex that highly qualified personnel assigned solely to this problem must be made available to work with our regulatory agencies—the Water Pollution Control Commission and the state Department of Health—in producing and enforcing acceptable standards which are the best possible reflection of all interests. The personnel must include socio-economic as well as scientific and engineering talent in order to relate and resolve all the conflicting uses of water in whatever standards may be produced. A substantial budget will be required to support this effort but the cost will be small in relation to the tremendous potential benefits accruing from more intelligent use of our water resources.

Industrial Waste Inventory

The foregoing discussion has been concerned chiefly with the technological problem of waste effect evaluation and the formulation of water quality standards and water use policies. One important technological detail in this general area should not be overlooked. This concerns the present lack of reliable data on the nature and quantity of industrial waste discharge. Such information is vitally important to sound water use regulation. To some extent this situation may be due to the historical reluctance of industry to make such data publicly available, and from this standpoint industrial operational policy is involved. To a greater extent, however, the situation is one of lack of facilities for determining the character and quantity of wastes produced. Such facilities should be as much a part of the industrial plant as the regular production line and should be operated with the same degree of attention. Complex studies will be a part of water quality standard determination. It will be to industry's advantage to see that the studies are based on reliable information.

POLITICAL, SOCIAL, AND ECONOMIC CONSIDERATIONS

Previous discussion has recognized the existence of competing and conflicting uses of the water resource. Resolution of these conflicts into water quality standards which reflect the best use of the resource is essential. Technology must provide the factual information upon which best use determinations are made but technology must be supplemented by the socioeconomic disciplines in evaluating this information.

There are other political, social, and economic considerations operating in conjunction with technological considerations that concern industry and its relation to other water resource users. Some of these are related to problems of best use determination, but others have to do with development subsequent to best use and water quality standard determination.

They include:

1. Recognition of differences in economic bases between the private and public areas and the effect of these differences on policy formulation and implementation.
2. Allocation of whatever pollution absorbing capacity may be defined by adopted water quality standards among different and competing contributors.

Economic Base Differences

Determination of cost of pollution abatement is an essential step at several points in a program development. For example:

1. Definition of best use will require cost-benefit analyses to show the economic benefits derived from a given degree of abatement compared with the cost of abatement.
2. Alternative methods of achieving any specified degree of abatement usually exist. Choice between these alternatives is usually based on cost considerations.

Costs and benefits are usually calculated on an annual basis or on some time-dependent basis. In the case of public works pollution abatement projects and resulting public benefits, costs and benefits are calculated on time periods ranging from twenty to forty years. However, in the case of privately financed industrial works, periods for annual cost and relative feasibility determination are much shorter, rarely more than five years and frequently only two years. The shorter industrial period arises from the profound effect of corporate taxes and the corresponding necessity to consider as economically feasible only those capital improvements whose saving will return the investment cost in a very short time. Annual costs consist of the annual amortization of the original investment plus annual operating costs. Obviously the shorter periods result in much higher amortization costs. For example, if money is worth 5 per cent, annual amortization cost on a five-year basis will be 23.1 per cent of the investment compared to 8.0 per cent on a twenty-year basis. In other words industry is accustomed to working from a base on which the investment amortization factor of annual cost is at least four times that commonly considered in public works.

This difference is a complicating factor in cost-benefit studies. If the accelerated payoff philosophy of industry is applied to cost-benefit analyses of industrial waste abatement, it is apparent that a lower degree of abatement can be economically justified than in the case of the lower amortization rate used for public works projects. The existence of this complication was recognized during the 1965 Western Resources Conference at Fort Collins, Colorado, by several speakers from the economics field. There was general advocacy by these speakers of long-time comparison periods for *both* public and industrial situations. However, such an approach throws on industry a disproportionate share of cost responsibility for the abstract, nonquantitative benefits which must be justified by considerations other than simple economics. This is a conflicting viewpoint that will have to be resolved in formulating a water use policy and water quality standards.

Another effect of this difference in economic base appears in the choice among alternative methods of achieving whatever degree of abatement may be required. The short-term industrial analysis period favors those methods whose capital cost is low even though very substantially higher operating costs may be involved. This is quite the opposite of public-works practice. This has such implications as:

1. In the case of separate industrial waste treatment, plants using less conventional, higher capacity processes even though more highly skilled operation is involved, regulatory agencies must be prepared to accept these less conventional systems.

2. In the case of joint industrial-municipal treatment, industry's position will affect the design and operating policies of the system.

An example of such a possibility for biological secondary treatment is the potential of the high-capacity, completely mixed, activated sludge process compared with the trickling filters classically favored in Iowa. Research at the University of Iowa is demonstrating feasibility of high-degree secondary treatment at one-hour aeration periods. This process requires less than 10 per cent of the volume of structures required for conventional filtration. The capital cost savings potential is correspondingly large and more than enough to offset the higher cost of power and more skilled operation.

Biologically treatable industrial wastes yield to the same basic treatment methods as those applied to municipal wastes. However, it is quite likely that the growing influence of the industrial factor with its different economic viewpoint may bring about a marked change from the methods to which Iowa is accustomed for treatment of such wastes. Obviously, nonbiologically treatable wastes with specialized treatment problems will be more frequently encountered.

Allocation of Pollution Assimilation Capacity

A knotty problem, which does not seem to have been satisfactorily resolved in areas which already have water quality standards, is allocation of an allowable pollutional load on a water resource among the various contributors. This becomes important in the cases where industrial load is a large portion of the total load, as is the case in many Iowa locations.

For example, there are Iowa situations where primary treatment of the municipal waste is sufficient to meet established stream standards. However, separately treated industrial wastes create an additional pollutional load requiring high-degree treatment to meet the total stream requirements. Is it reasonable to expect the municipality to provide complete treatment in order to release some of the stream's assimilative capacity so that industrial treatment requirements may be lowered?

Questions of this nature will probably have to be answered on the merits of each instance. However, the provision of whatever guidelines are possible as a part of the state's water policy formulation will most certainly be desirable.

SUMMARY

Iowa industry already generates organic wastes having a pollutional effect of more than twice the present population. In addition nonorganic wastes associated with metal processing and various chemically oriented industries are creating locally severe problems. The state's prospects for industrial growth foretell increased severity of the industrial waste problem, both as to frequency of occurrence and magnitude.

In spite of the existing magnitude of industrial waste production, present industrial activity is distributed over the state and waste-related problems are more of a local nature rather than widespread. The present status is such that the nature of control and regulation can be largely preventive rather than exclusively corrective. This is a much more favorable situation than that associated with widespread regionally critical conditions in heavily industrialized metropolitan regions. It can work to the advantage of all concerned if wisely pursued, but immediate action is necessary to use this advantage.

The principal problems are those associated with formulation and implementation of policy concerning use of the state's water resources. Important policy questions concern the evaluation and integration of various conflicting uses into a system of quality standards which reflect the best use of various parts of our water resources. This action is significant to all producers of waterborne pollution but it is especially significant to industry since these standards will have important bearing on the nature of industrial expansion. Recognized and dependable standards are necessary for firm planning.

The principal technological problems are those associated with evaluating the effect of various industrial and municipal waste constituents on other uses of water resources. Quantitative information is necessary to determine the degree of abatement required for any given combination of uses. This will involve substantial time and talent for which funds must be made available.

An immediate step which can be taken is an inventory of present industrial waste production. This is a responsibility which industry can reasonably be expected to assume. Installation and operation of metering and monitoring facilities will be required. The data must be made available to the proper authority for use in formulating and implementing water use policy.

Unique problems are created by the differences in economic base between industrial and public areas. These differences need to be recognized in such matters as cost-benefit analyses and method comparison. The differences will tend to favor low-investment, high-capacity installations, requiring a somewhat higher degree of operation than normally associated with more conventional methods for comparable wastes. These factors should be considered in any pollution regulations which may be adopted by regulatory agencies.

Many of the matters discussed herein are applicable to public as well as industrial pollution problems. The rapid evolution of an industrial economy in Iowa, however, provides the impetus for bringing them into focus for immediate action. This is industry's unique contribution to Iowa's water pollution problem. Movement toward a comprehensive and fair water use policy is, perhaps, industry's most urgent need if it is to assume its proper role in water pollution control and abatement.

DISCUSSION

RALPH W. RANSOM

A POLLUTION CONTROL PROGRAM IN A MEAT PACKING PLANT REQUIRES continual persuasion and activity. Benefits, such as reducing costs and increasing product quality and volume, may not be immediately recognizable to supervisors and plant employees.

Pollution control can be an economic asset through the saving of product and improvement in product quality. Permitting pollution to occur results in degradation or loss of salvageable materials and a higher cost of waste disposal.

PREVENTION

Many plants have their own water supply because the cost is less than if water were purchased from a public supply. Water from a private supply is not free by any means. However, little attention is given to excessive use. The detrimental effects of excessive water use include:

1. The hydraulic requirements of subsequent handling and treating equipment are increased.
2. Water requirements and costs are excessive.
3. Fuel costs for water heating are multiplied.
4. Larger quantities of product ingredients are carried away as waste thus increasing the total pollution load.
5. More water is wasted.

Technological developments have affected water use and pollution both favorably and adversely. Some developments have decreased water utilization while others have increased water requirements. For example, decreased utilization resulted when heating in an atmosphere of steam replaced submerged cooking and when refrigerated water for product chilling was recirculated instead of being used only once. In contrast, increased water utilization has resulted from washing operations in conveyor machines which require greater volumes of water as compared to washing by hand.

Maintaining sanitary conditions is not as closely associated with the use of larger volumes of water as in times past. However, this is a water use that requires close attention. The practice of using a stream of water for its hydraulic cleaning effect is difficult to overcome. Good sanitation practice requires a thorough job of "dry cleaning" to remove

RALPH W. RANSOM is manager, Ottumwa Industrial Airport, Ottumwa, Iowa.

pieces and particles, and labor required for this will be less than that required to manipulate a hose. The recent development of detergents has reduced water requirements for cleaning, particularly the need for hot water.

Comparing similar plants in the meat packing industry, water consumption per unit of production has been twice as much in some plants as in others. High consumption occurred in the plants with their own water supplies whereas those with low consumption purchased their water from a municipal supply.

Decreasing water utilization will generally increase the concentration of wastes but will decrease the total pollution load leaving the plant. In other words, if water flow is minimized, it will not be able to transport as much pollutional material from the manufacturing process.

Equipment currently in use aids in reducing wastage of processing materials or in their immediate salvage. Equipment has been developed which results in the release of rendered fat and its salvage from the product. This returns materials of higher quality to the production end since these fats have not had a chance to degrade before they reach the large plant system.

As previously stated, machines requiring increased volumes of water have been developed to ease labor requirements. In conjunction with these machines additional development has produced equipment that immediately treats the water used in these processes to remove and recover much of the pollutional material.

Pollution resulting from cleanup operations can be minimized by studying manufacturing operations so as to prevent wastes from reaching the stage where they become problems. Dry cleaning can return much material to one phase or another of the manufacturing operations and thus materially reduce pollution.

IN-PLANT WASTE TREATMENT

After all measures have been taken to reduce the volume and concentration of wastes at the source, it is necessary to consider what in-plant waste treatment can be provided to salvage materials of value and to reduce the pollution load requiring subsequent treatment. Reuse of some of the in-plant treated waste as condenser water may be possible. Admittedly, this may not reduce the volume of waste requiring treatment but it can materially reduce water consumption.

To maximize benefits of in-plant treatment, all polluted water must be handled rapidly and the collection system as well as the treatment equipment must be maintained at a high sanitary level. In addition, any recaptured material must be returned to the proper production department without delay to avoid degradation.

Generally, in-plant waste treatment is accomplished by three methods: (1) screening, (2) settling and skimming, and (3) aeroflotation.

Screening of certain flows has produced acceptable results when done close to the source of waste. This removes solids of greater value, and perhaps more of them, since the solids remain in the water a shorter period of time and are not subject to disintegration due to attrition. When close proximity to the source is not possible, screening previous to any further treatment is advantageous for the same reasons.

The most prevalent in-plant treatment system includes settling and skimming in basins which have detention times ranging from forty-five minutes to two hours. Constant or regular and frequent removal of accumulated settled solids and floating materials prevents their decomposition. In most cases, this operation is close enough to the source so that the recovered solids are usable in the manufacture of by-products. Good sanitation contributes much to its success.

A process known as aeroflotation, borrowed from the paper industry, has proven valuable in numerous plants. It usually follows settling and skimming since it removes the very finely divided solids.

MEASUREMENTS

No problem can be treated properly or solved without being well defined. Thus, for best control of waste volumes and concentrations continuous measurements must be obtained. Meters to measure not only total waste flows per twenty-four hours but also to indicate the degree and time of peaks are a necessity. Except in rare instances it is not practical to apply this requirement to individual areas in a plant. The total plant record will usually indicate troubles, and deduction leads the troubleshooters to the errant area.

SUMMARY

Pollution control and abatement must start at the source before the problem reaches unreasonable proportions. The source is that point where the water is used in the production operation or where it is converted by the operation from clean to polluted water. Efforts made at that point have side effects that can make them self-supporting or quite possibly yield a profit to the industry through a reduction in water consumption, a saving of materials used in manufacture, or a reduction in subsequent treatment.

Finally, the flow should be followed through the plant waste accumulating system, and measurements and analyses should be made to check the results of control at the source. Using the same data, the adequacy of treatment given before releasing the effluent to the receiving system can be determined.

DISCUSSION

KEITH A. McNURLEN

THE PROBLEM OF POLLUTION IS TODAY A SUDDEN-INTEREST SUBJECT TO millions of Americans, and most of them feel that it is something that has overtaken us suddenly and can be solved in a short time with our space-age technology.

Just how far have we progressed in the field of pollution control? We can all remember reading about medieval times when the safe and fashionable place to live was upstairs. The upstairs vista allowed you to dump your slop jars out the window, and gentlemanly courtesy of the time made it at least chivalrous to look before you dumped. Have we really progressed a great deal from this concept? Not really. Many are the towns today which collect their sewage and run it into a stream to plague their neighbors further downstream. Most collection is underground, otherwise we have only the slop jar technique on a larger scale slightly more refined.

The old cliché that dilution is the answer to pollution is passé. The modern age can be described as one of aquamania, or a craze for water. There was a time a few years ago when some people thought water was required only for use with Cutty Sark and their knowledge ended there. Today these same people look at water as an item in which to swim, on which to boat, under which to scuba dive, as a place by which to sit and watch a sunset or sunrise, and finally as an area of curiosity since it has suddenly become big news, especially in the East.

The sooner we realize that we cannot continue to load our streams, landfill and bulldoze our open spaces, and pollute our air and not reach an irreversible saturation point, the better it will be for all; and as our other authors indicate, the time for that decision is now.

I would like to delve briefly into the history of the Izaak Walton League of America to illustrate a point on pollution. Formed in 1923 to combat pollution, the League's first surveys showed 85 per cent of our inland streams were polluted even then, and yet only 31 per cent of the nation was sewered at the time. So we cannot today point at a segment of the population and say, "You did it."

Since pollution is a people-caused phenomenon, we must look to the people to finance the cleanup demanded by our age of aquamania. Perhaps if we could go to offending cities and cause a reverse flow of

KEITH A. McNURLEN is commissioner, Iowa Conservation Commission, and a member of the National Board of Directors, Izaak Walton League of America.

a bathtub-size slug of sewage down the hall stairs and padlock offending industries, we would get some action. Certainly, we would get a lot of reaction and a tiger by the tail. Between this extreme and the do-nothing approach lies the gray area where the compromises must be made.

Will Rogers once said, "We are all ignorant—only about different things." Have you ever applied that thought to pollution and seen how amazingly accurate it is? There are people who are world recognized as authorities on pollution, and yet there are hundreds of polluting chemicals about which they know little or absolutely nothing as to tolerances. Fish toxicants can be cited, Bidrin can be cited, as can the example of Clear Lake in California where chemical buildup reached 250,000 times the applied dosage.

The Water Quality Act of 1965 is another effort to improve our record. Yet, if you check our streams, our air, our lakes, and our oceans, we really are not even keeping up because pollution is like conservation—you have to move fast in order to stand still and not regress.

The final item that I hope we never find in the pollution problem, be it private, municipal, or industrial, is the attitude of the courts as described by Senator McClellan on his crime commission reports. One jurist said he once felt the way to settle tax inequities was to throw out all the laws, then we would get rid of all selfish-interest legislation. We have in Iowa the golden opportunity to set up our laws on a preventive basis, which is certainly to be preferred over corrective legislation, and I hope that those in our state who are charged with attracting industry will lay it on the line that we expect our waters to remain clean and pure. We have enough of a problem to clean up what we now have in pollution and, unlike the Community Chest, we want no more contributions by others.

So, in conclusion, the question is asked again, "Where does the responsibility lie for cleaning up our waters?" The answer is plain and simple. Every city and town and every industry is responsible for cleaning up the pollution it creates.

CHAPTER 10

AGRICULTURAL POLLUTION— SOURCES AND CONTROL

GEORGE M. BROWNING

WATER IS VITAL TO THE HEALTH, SAFETY, AND ECONOMIC WELL-BEING of 194 million Americans. Present and future economic growth at the local, state, and national level depends on how well we develop and use our water resources. In total we are well blessed with water, but the problem is that it is not always distributed at the right place or at the right time to satisfy needs and wants as the population and economy grows.

Water problems are complex and dynamic and do not end at the man-made political boundaries of a city, a county, or a state. There is no single or final solution to the water problems, so that programs, to be effective, must be flexible and accommodate change whether it be from new technology, changing consumer preference, population growth, weather cycles, or a host of other factors.

Local, state, and federal governments have a responsibility and must play an important role in the development of our water resources. But the facts are that effective use of the nation's and Iowa's water resources will not be realized until all people, rural and urban alike, with vested or socioeconomic interest are willing to reflect their decisions on long-range programs for the improvement and management of our water resources.

People in general are not as concerned as they should be, or would be, about water resources if they really understood the

GEORGE M. BROWNING is regional director, North-central Agricultural Experiment Stations, Iowa State University. The author is indebted to staff members at Iowa State University for much of the information included in this chapter.

150

problems and realized the stake, the responsibility, and the opportunity that they have in helping plan for more effective development, maintenance, and use of an adequate supply of high-quality water. Conservation, management, and quality maintenance of water resources is not an independent, individual problem but one of equal importance to urban and rural citizens alike. To assure that our water resources are developed, protected, and used for the common good and best public interest, a coordinated, cooperative approach on a community or watershed basis is required.

An overall program to plan and develop our water resources must provide for collection and interpretation of data; the practical development and use of laws; mechanisms for making good decisions; coordination of local, state, federal, and private interests and activities; and local understanding and participation. With this general background let us consider some of the problems and some of the things that agricultural users can do for control of pollution of Iowa's water resources.

AGRICULTURE'S NEEDS AND RESPONSIBILITIES

Agriculture is the largest single user of the water reaching the land as rain or snowfall. Directly or indirectly, the operations on Iowa's farmlands are the greatest potential source of pollutants to our water supply. Thus agriculture has a major responsibility and obligation to develop practices and programs for the most efficient use of our water supply without endangering its quality.

Farmers on the thousands of small watersheds are the custodians of land and water resources that are the source of our surface water supply. These resources provide food, fiber, timber, water, wildlife, shelter, and much of the outdoor recreation for our population. Runoff from these watersheds fills our reservoirs for agricultural, municipal, and industrial uses.

Sediment, a product of improper land use, is the largest single pollutant of the nation's streams and reservoirs. Sediment damages fish and wildlife, reduces reservoir storage capacity, clogs highway and drainage ditches, and fills stream channels, thereby increasing flood hazards and adding to the cost of cleanup following floods and to the removal of sediment from domestic and industrial supplies.

Floods originate in these watersheds and not in the major river channels. Floods that damage land, crops, livestock, buildings, fish, wildlife, domestic and industrial water supplies, and roads or bridges result in smaller tax revenues and increase the necessary public expenditures for repair or replacement. Floods may endanger health and safety by disrupting public utility services or by making drinking water unsafe in both rural and urban areas. Much of this damage can be eliminated with adequate upstream land and water management.

Until recently, people in the humid part of the United States had taken their water supplies for granted, along with air and sunlight, as unlimited gifts of nature. Of greatest concern has been the loss of life and property from floods which are the result of temporary water surpluses. However, in recent years aggravated by moisture deficiencies, pollution, and growing demand on limited water supply, people are gradually realizing that water can be a *scarce* resource and that steps must be taken to determine the *rights of control, privileges of use,* and *better ways and means* for more *effective utilization.* We can not change the amount, intensity, and distribution of rain and snowfall. The job then is to adopt measures that minimize their detrimental effects and improve the beneficial effects of water for all segments of our society.

In recent years soil and water conservation programs have done much to reduce the runoff from our agricultural lands. These programs not only reduce flooding and sedimentation but conserve moisture by storing it in the soil for use by crops or by recharging our ground-water supplies. Land treatment measures, including cropping systems, tillage, contouring, terracing, and other practices not only are needed to tie down the soil and conserve the rainfall but also to help control runoff and contribute to flood control. These treatments are very important but they alone will solve only a part of the problem. Large dams on our major streams and smaller dams and water control structures on smaller tributaries and watersheds are essential to a sound water resource use program.

WATER POLLUTION FROM EROSION

Three of every four acres of Iowa's land area are cropland and almost one-half of this is planted annually to corn and soybeans. Heavy rains of high intensity occur frequently in May and June. Corn and soybean plants are small at this time of year and afford little protection to the soil. The result is runoff laden with sediment which finds its way into streams and reservoirs, resulting in loss of storage capacity and impairing the quality of the water. Sediment is related to the type of soil, the type of vegetation, and the use made of conservation practices. For example, the Corps of Engineers found the average sediment load over a 12-year period at Pisgah, Iowa, to be equivalent to 17 tons per acre per year from the 417-square-mile Soldier watershed. In contrast the sediment load measured on a 23-square-mile watershed at East Fork, Hardin Creek, near Churdan averaged only .05 tons per acre per year for the period of record.

Most of the sediment is derived from sheet erosion, but in western Iowa up to half of the sediment discharged is from gullies.

The effect of vegetation and conservation is illustrated by comparing the results from three field-sized watersheds at the cooperative state-federal hyrologic station near Treynor, Iowa. An unterraced, 80-acre watershed in continuous corn produced 30 tons per acre of sediment in 1964, while a watershed in grass produced only a trace of sediment. A comparable watershed in corn, but terraced, produced about one-third the surface runoff and relatively little sediment.

Studies by the Soil Conservation Service on the Mule Creek watershed in southwest Iowa show the life of small reservoirs may be one-third their designed life if the planned land treatments are not completed. Loss of reservoir storage is relatively less on large reservoirs than on small ones but still can be a serious problem in areas of steep, highly erosive soil unless land treatments are applied.

Fortunately, pollution of surface water by erosion can be controlled with application of known agricultural practices and structures. The relative effect of each agricultural practice can be predicted by the use of an erosion equation. The problem is basically one of how to use control measures most economically, and how to convince people that it should be done. Year-around close growing vegetative cover essentially eliminates sheet erosion, but how does a farmer make a living in Iowa raising cover crops? Contour farming, listing, strip cropping, and terracing reduce or nearly eliminate erosion. However, much land is farmed with little regard to these practices because of lack of capital, nuisance of farming in a prescribed manner, irregular topography not adaptable to conventional conservation practices, short tenure, insufficient benefits, and other personal reasons.

We know how to control erosion. Much progress has been made by Iowa's 100 soil conservation districts in applying erosion control practices. But erosion still continues at an excessive rate in parts of Iowa, emphasizing the need for stepped-up activity. We need to develop new and imaginative methods for erosion control on areas of irregular topography where conventional control methods are not practical. The answer involves minimization of the time when the poorly protected soil is exposed to rainfall and application of measures, through tillage or construction, which reduce movement of soil and water to and from channels. Possibly, better answers are to be found for some areas in broadcast or narrow-row corn and soybeans, mulch tillage techniques, complete water control by tillage, or movement of earth to reduce slopes and trap sediment. More study on physical variations of present methods and aspects of economics and law is needed. Innovations involving completely different approaches such as plant genetics, soil stabilizers, earth moving, or storage and sub-surface removal of water may eventually be used.

WATER POLLUTION FROM CROP PRODUCTION

Iowa is blessed with a reasonably favorable climate and productive soils. To capitalize on these resources, Iowa farmers traditionally have devoted a high percentage of land area to the production of corn, soybeans, oats, and forages. As mentioned previously, corn and soybeans are grown on 15.2 million acres in Iowa. The large acreage of corn and the rapid shift in recent years from oats to soybeans reflect the economic advantage of these crops under Iowa conditions. The acreage of corn and soybeans grown in Iowa is likely to increase in the future if economic forces are free to move crop production to areas where they can be produced most efficiently.

Regardless of whether or not this happens, Iowa still has a challenge and an opportunity to help provide roughly an additional $20 million worth of farm commodities to feed an additional 60 million Americans by 1980. In addition there is a vast market provided by the 500 million people who live in the relatively more prosperous free-world countries. But the real challenge and opportunity is to help develop markets to supply the 2 billion people in the free world who are hungry every night.

Agricultural exports from the United States totaled $6.1 billion for the year ending June 30, 1964. This is equivalent to the products from one out of every four acres. Iowa has the land, the skills, the technology, and the manpower to produce more for world markets than we are doing. We have both a financial and a humanitarian stake in seeing that this is done. Assuming the same trends in the future as in the past, crop output is expected to increase 34 per cent by 1980. The cash receipts from crops in Iowa were $691 million in 1964. Most of the increased productivity will come from the use of more fertilizers, lime, herbicides, insecticides, and other products of modern technology.

Fertilizer usage in Iowa increased from 654,000 tons in 1954 to 1.3 million tons in 1964. Estimated usage in 1980 is 2.5 million tons. Rate of application per acre and the number of acres fertilized will increase as farmers strive for greater efficiency of production. Nitrogen is the keystone to intensified corn production. Eventually 1 million tons annually will be used in Iowa. Regardless of the form in which it is applied, it is soon changed to nitrates, which are soluble and free to move with percolating water.

The use of insecticides in Iowa increased sixfold from 1954 to 1964 and is expected to almost double the 1964 usage by 1980 as shown in Table 10.1. Iowa used 5.75 million pounds of herbicides in 1964 and projected usage is expected to be 10 million pounds by 1980. The use of fungicides in Iowa is small in comparison with other agricultural chemicals. It is estimated that Iowa used 20,000 pounds in 1964 with a projected usage of 25,000 pounds in 1980. If the

TABLE 10.1 INSECTICIDE USE IN 1954 AND 1964 AND PROJECTED USE IN 1970 AND 1980, IOWA.

Year	Applied to the Soil (1,000 lbs.)	Applied to Plants (1,000 lbs.)	Total (1,000 lbs.)
1954	180	870	1,050
1964	5,700	300	6,000
1970	8,000	500	8,500
1980	10,000	1,000	11,000

projected usages of agricultural chemicals for 1980 are realized, the possibilities of their use becoming more of a factor in water pollution will increase unless wise and judicious procedures and practices are used.

Now, let us examine some of the specific problems of the use of agricultural chemicals and what can be done to reduce or prevent their being a factor in pollution of Iowa's water resources. Agricultural chemicals are applied to soil, plants, animals, and buildings. Chlorinated hydrocarbon insecticides have limited solubility in water; organophosphates are somewhat more soluble; herbicides are even more soluble. Even though the amounts are very small, they move in water and can be measured with the gas chromotography technique. Some persist in their original form for considerable periods of time; others break down or are modified by microorganisms soon after application.

Iowa is in a climate belt where there is a net movement of water through the soil profile. Therefore, it may be postulated that during periods of excess moisture part of the soluble compounds enter the groundwater. But quantitative information is not available to show if this is so or to what extent or where and under what conditions there has been pollution so that corrective measures can be applied. We also need to know if practices anticipated for future use are likely to create problems so that preventive measures can be adopted.

Although real progress has been made in soil and water conservation, runoff and erosion still are serious problems. Soluble and insoluble materials are carried from farmlands in runoff water and sediment. These accumulate and concentrate in streams and reservoirs reducing storage capacity and impairing water quality. Extensive studies have been made of the problems, processes, and control methods of conserving soil and water. But there is little specific information on the amount of pollutants in runoff water and sediment or on the effects of water quality on the health of man. More studies are needed to determine to what extent this is a problem and to develop control methods.

Pesticides promote health directly through the control of vector-borne diseases. Indirectly, pesticides have made a great impact by facilitating the production and protection of food, feed, and fiber in greater quantity and quality and by keeping in check many kinds of nuisance insects and unwanted plants. In spite of all these benefits extensive use of any biologically active chemical implies a potential hazard which has to be evaluated. There is no question as to the toxicity of some organic pesticides even at very low concentrations.

Accumulating evidence indicates occurrence of pesticides in surface water, and to a lesser extent in groundwater, originating from land drainage, industrial waste discharge, purposeful application to water, and accidents. The presence of pesticides in water may be chronic but usually has been found to be at levels less than one part per billion. For short periods of time they frequently are present at higher concentrations.

Pesticide pollution of water has been studied most extensively in the southeastern states. Reports of farm pond fish kills were reported soon after 1945 when DDT and other organic pesticides became available to the public. In 1950 extensive fish kills occurred almost simultaneously in fourteen streams tributary to the Tennessee River in Alabama. Investigations showed that these kills were caused by insecticides washed from cotton fields following a series of intense rainstorms that produced large amounts of runoff. Although the common impression is that "pesticides getting in water" is responsible for all fish kills, this is not the case. The Public Health Service found that only 13–19 per cent of the 400–500 fish kills reported from 1961–64 were from this source.

How extensively are pesticides used in Iowa as compared with the southeast where most of the pollution has been reported? The rate of application per acre is about the same. But essentially 100 per cent of the cotton acreage is treated annually, whereas in Iowa only 2 per cent of the corn is treated for corn borer and 50 per cent of the acreage for corn rootworms. This suggests that surface water pollution from pesticides in Iowa has not reached the proportions it has in the South. But in Iowa increased usage is expected which will increase the potential for pollution unless preventive measures are adopted.

In general herbicides are of a relatively low order of toxicity, are relatively easily decomposed by soil microorganisms in about six months, and are metabolized by plants. Thus the potential of these compounds for being a source of pollution is minimized. Studies have shown an appreciable loss of herbicides in the runoff water from experimental plots when simulated rainfall was applied to sloping erosible land that had a preemergence herbicide treatment immediately before the application of simulated rain. The extreme conditions of the experimental plots seldom occur in actual practice but can be experienced if heavy rains come soon after the chemicals are applied to soil or plants.

Water quality management today faces greater problems than at any time in history. In addition to the natural contaminants there are present as pollutants in our waters multiple chemical substances, products of our modern technology. These pollutants take on greater significance as the growing population and industrial economy increase the demand on our water supply.

We need studies to evaluate occurrence of pesticides in both ground and surface water to learn:

1. How specific pesticides enter water and why, and which ones contaminate water and which ones do not. This information will tell us which pesticides are safe to use, and where, from a water quality standpoint.
2. What the effects are on humans and animals when they consume water contaminated with pesticides.
3. Which pesticides can and cannot be removed from our water supplies by current treatment practices.
4. How extensively groundwater is contaminated by pesticides and what the nature and significance of such contamination is.
5. How pesticide pollution can be controlled.

Pesticides will be considered potentially dangerous until their long-term impacts, singly and in combination, on biological behavior can be understood more completely. Things that may be done to control pesticide pollution include:

1. Improve legal control of aerial application of pesticides where needed.
2. Improve the education of pesticide users.
3. Improve soil conservation practices, especially as they relate to retardation of surface runoff.

4. Use short-lived pesticides where possible.
5. Develop more selectively toxic chemicals and biological control methods.
6. Learn how to use nonchemical pest control methods more effectively.

WATER POLLUTION FROM LIVESTOCK PRODUCTION

Historically, Iowa has been a major livestock producing state with increasing output over the years. Iowa holds a position of leadership within a leading geographical area of livestock production, an area which promises to accelerate and widen this gap of leadership in the years ahead. Fertile soil; favorable climate; crop and animal production know-how; less pressure from urbanization; decreasing dependence on proximity to markets and consumption centers as a result of improved transportation, processing, and storage techniques; and decentralization of livestock processing centers all are contributory factors to this increasing leadership.

Iowa leads the nation in the production of livestock and livestock products. Safeguarding the quantity and quality of these products, for safe human consumption, from possible effects of waterborne contamination is equally as important as preservation of the water supplies. Cash receipts from Iowa's livestock and related products were $1.357 billion in 1955 and $1.977 billion in 1964. Demands for livestock and livestock products at home and abroad continue to increase and the value of Iowa's output is expected to increase to $2.622 billion by 1975. Currently, the number of animals on Iowa farms includes 7.3 million cattle and calves, 14.0 million hogs, 1.3 million sheep and lambs, 19.0 million chickens, and 8 million turkeys.

Water consumption by domestic animals is estimated at 105 million gallons in 1965 and is expected to increase to 156 million gallons by 1975. Water quality influences the health, productivity, and performance of an animal. Total salt, sulfate, and nitrate content; temperature; and the existence of numerous chemicals and organisms are a few examples of water properties which affect its pathogenicity and palatability when consumed by livestock. Several of these properties are undesirably modified by introduced pollutants of various origin. Some undesirable properties are found in unpolluted, natural groundwater.

High-quality water is a must in the dairy food industry. Many of the microorganisms with which water may be contaminated, while not pathogenic to man, can be highly destructive to the food with which they come in contact. Contaminated water supplies have been a frequent cause of spoilage of butter and they present serious problems to cottage cheese manufacturers in many locations. The microorganisms produce objectionable flavor, odor, and color defects which drastically lower the quality of the products and their shelf life. The fluid milk industry, which derives its raw materials from hundreds of thousands of farms producing milk, is a good example of an industry which must take elaborate measures to limit the microbial content of its water supply, principally to protect the health of its customers. The U.S. Public Health Service recommends, as do most all state and municipal milk ordinances, a specific and maximum coliform count of 2.2/100 milliliters. They also give detailed specifications for the location, construction, and operation of dug and drilled wells and for the design and operation of pumps on dairy farms producing under Grade A ordinance.

It is estimated that the manure production of livestock on Iowa farms in 1965 amounts to 90–100 million tons. Probably about one-half of the livestock droppings are on pasture and uncultivated ground and one-half in pens, feedlots, and loafing areas. Increased automation and efficiency of crop use are expected to increase the latter fraction, but at the same time intensified production methods permit more complete control of wastes through properly designed disposal facilities. Disposal of farm wastes creates a potential source of pollution for both surface and underground water supplies.

Confinement production of livestock and poultry in lots, yards, and buildings rather than on pasture or range, frequently results in large volumes of accumulated animal excreta and associated feed, water, and bedding or litter wastes within or near the production unit. These concentrated animal wastes are potential sources of undesirable pollution to groundwater and surface water supplies until such time as they are thinly spread over the soil surface or incorporated with the soil. Even then some minor undesirable pollution can occur, but it is usually not within the reasonable control of the livestock producer.

The pollution potential is greatest when the wastes are allowed to accumulate or are stored on the ground surface in a lot or yard where rainfall can leach or detach and transport portions of the animal waste materials with surface runoff or soil infiltrate. Studies of water pollution of streams from feedlot runoff indicate that the runoff is characterized by a high oxygen demand, high ammonia content, and heavy bacterial populations. The pollution problem is intermittent since it occurs during and following runoff, but it causes a severe slugging effect on the stream. Serious depletion of the dissolved oxygen content of the stream may occur, especially if the stream is small or the waste load is large.

Surface water pollution by feedlot runoff can be minimized by (1) frequent removal of accumulated excrement, (2) diverting all runoff from points of higher elevation around or under the feedlot so that only the precipitation falling directly into the lot causes runoff, and (3) construction of a settling basin or desilting area through which all runoff must flow.

Pollution of groundwater to some degree within a localized area is highly probable whenever accumulations of animal wastes are stored on or below the ground surface unless the wastes are stored in a watertight structure. Soil infiltrate from unsurfaced feedlots, manure piles, animal waste treatment lagoons, and liquid manure storage tanks which are not watertight or any water transporting soluble materials to the groundwater table (the surface of the zone of saturation) will contribute pollutants along with the groundwater recharge.

Undesirable groundwater pollution can be minimized or avoided by (1) storage of all potential pollutants in watertight structures, (2) frequent removal of soil surface stored animal wastes, and (3) proper handling and disposal of all chemicals and wastes to prevent spillage and other accidents whereby concentrated solutions are introduced into the soil or directly into the groundwater supplies.

Complete prevention of groundwater pollution is an unreasonable expectation, at least through the next several decades. However, every reasonable attempt should be made to minimize pollution; to delineate localized areas of polluted groundwater; to properly close abandoned wells, improperly located and constucted wells, and other openings which serve as portals of pollution entry into groundwater supplies; and to properly locate and construct new water wells so that their areas of influence do not overlap known or suspected areas of polluted groundwater.

DISCUSSION

CLYDE M. BERRY

Dr. George M. Browning has pinpointed very well the major sources of pollution in an agricultural setting—erosion, crop production, and livestock production. He has listed many specifics in each area and to these I agree. He has offered positive remedial measures in each area—and I agree. He has noted many areas where additional research

Clyde M. Berry is associate director, Institute of Agricultural Medicine, University of Iowa, Iowa City, Iowa.

is needed—and I agree. There is little to be added to his comments except to caution against assuming that progress in the area of water pollution control will be in small logical, sequential increments—a projection of what we have accomplished in the decades, generations, and centuries just past.

As a boy I read science fiction and enjoyed the comic strip that had to be censored during World War II in order not to give away any military way-out secrets to the enemy. So many impossible things have happened in my lifetime that my innate conservatism and my emotional and intellectual agreement with Dr. Browning's paper suffers from a modicum of reservation. Just because something has not been done or is wildly impractical at the present time is no assurance that it may not be in our future. All of us have seen the immutable chemical law of conservation of matter "repealed" with the advent of the atomic age. The limitless sea has become a commercial source for magnesium and bromine. The ownership of the airspace above a country becomes a little out of date when satellites are orbiting the earth.

Ancient shibboleths will probably die a hard, lingering death. Our legal systems and especially our concepts of "property" may experience substantial revision. As we solve the problem of weather control we will have the new problem of who now truly owns the rain—and from whom was it taken? At that time will a farmer who owns the land own the rain that falls on it? Will erosion control be on a much grander scale and compulsory?

Highway departments seem to be developing a broader viewpoint and a social conscience and the superroad of tomorrow may very well be an integrated portion of a large erosion control project. After all, why should not a highway embankment also serve as a dam if it is in the interest of the public?

If our aquanauts are taking us into a new era where the oceans will be "farmed," we might be on the brink of a new era where fresh water impoundments will be created and "farmed." The lowlands we have drained may be restored and new and different "crops" may be raised. How do we know? Have we ever really tried?

Dr. Browning speaks of an increasing use of farm chemicals and of how they leach away and what happens when they do. Can we be sure that insecticide and herbicide application in the future will not become an intensive pin-point application and not the broad spectrum fill-the-air, fill-the-soil approach that the late Rachel Carson alleged and deplored? I suspect that developments within the next generation, especially in biological control, will make current practices seem as primitive as yesterday's wooden plow.

Why can not we envision mammoth earth moving projects that

will result in such a uniform grade that, along with equally huge and imaginative drainage and flood control efforts, they can accomplish a type of erosion control that would not be now considered possible? Why cannot we envision predigested animal feeds that will tremendously reduce the size of our great, and growing, manure disposal problem? Why cannot we envision chemurgy advancing to the point where animal excreta, perhaps for their hormone content or as a bacterial substrate for further processing, may not be more valuable than will be the animal carcass for food?

Dr. Browning has provided an able appraisal of water pollution problems associated with agriculture and aptly projects these into the future. As stated earlier, I agree but continue to be haunted by the implications of our continuing industrial revolution. This feeling of disquiet is extended to a revolution in agriculture which, it would seem, has only begun and which will have profound implications on the whole subject of water pollution, particularly on that portion relating to agriculture.

DISCUSSION

ROBERT C. RUSSELL

DR. GEORGE M. BROWNING HAS ABLY PRESENTED AN EXTREMELY important and necessary facet of the pollution problem. He has covered the subject very well, and his information and views on agricultural needs and responsibilities and water pollution from erosion and crop and livestock production have taken us in a very forthright manner to the heart of the problem in the area of pollution control by agricultural users. This has been done so well that it would be redundant to dwell to any great extent on his discussion. Perhaps the importance of this area of pollution control and abatement can best be substantiated and affirmed by excerpting some of the conservation policies of the Izaak Walton League of America (as revised January 1, 1964) that pertain to this area and offering a few additional points for consideration.

These policies and principles indicate the league's interest and concern in water as it relates to agriculture. This is not a fleeting interest, but one that has been developing in the league's conserva-

ROBERT C. RUSSELL is executive secretary, Iowa Division, Izaak Walton League of America.

tion program since its inception forty-three years ago. While these are the conservation policies of the Izaak Walton League of America, they also represent the opinion of a great many people regarding pollution and its abatement.

These excerpts taken from the *Conservation Policies of the Izaak Walton League of America,* pp. 6–11, should also be prefaced by noting that basically the Izaak Walton League has the following policy. "The natural resources of America should be managed and used to provide to the people the greatest benefits of all kinds in the long run."

In soil conservation the league is guided by the following principles:

1. The public interest requires that all capabilities of each acre of land should be recognized in planning for its optimum use, and that such planning must include consideration of the interests of individual private landowners.

2. A watershed is a logical unit for planning conservation and development of soil and related resources.

Concerning water conservation principles:

1. Ideally, all water should be fit for direct human use—drinking, swimming, esthetic enjoyment—without special treatment, and it will then also be eminently suited for municipal, agricultural, and industrial utilization.

2. Water is inseparably bound to the land insofar as its development, management, and use are concerned.

Regarding irrigation:

1. The League supports irrigation which is of overall public benefit, but recognizes that irrigation is not always a necessary and desirable use of water.

2. Generally speaking, land should not be irrigated if it cannot pay its way, or if the waters involved are more valuable for other purposes.

Pollution and pesticides control principles:

1. The public interest requires that Man shall not act to so pollute his environment that it is rendered unfit for his direct use or esthetic enjoyment, or for fish, wildlife, and other organisms.

2. Intensive research programs should be established to determine the effects—both direct and indirect, immediate and cumulative—upon man and all living things of all known and potential water and air pollutants and pesticides, chemical and otherwise.

3. Intensive research programs should be established to determine sure methods for control of pesticides and for removal from water and air of all known and potential pollutants, chemical and otherwise. Legislation to control environmental pollution of all varieties should be based on the results of such research.

4. There should be comprehensive public information programs at Federal, State, and local levels to promote better and more widespread

understanding of all environmental pollution problems and of the needs for action.

Water pollution:

1. There is no sound justification for water pollution. The people of the United States are entitled to wholesome water, usable for all human needs.

2. Ground-water should be equally considered with surface water in planning for control and prevention of pollution.

3. The League strives to prevent and reduce pollution of water by sediment and similar matter, as well as that by chemicals and other materials.

* * * *

5. The public goal should be maximum removal of pollutants from all streams, rather than use of streams to carry an "acceptable maximum" load of wastes.

6. Since water courses know no political boundaries, pollution control is rightfully a Federal as well as a local, State, and interstate responsibility. Although control measures should be initiated at the lowest effective level, the Federal Government should have clear authority to strongly enforce pollution abatement and prevention in cases when lower authority proves ineffectual or inadequate.

7. Adequate and workable State water pollution control laws are a necessity, and the utmost in reasonable enforcement of such laws must be attained in every State.

* * * * *

12. There should be laws which require that domestic, agricultural, and industrial chemicals and other products which are extremely resistant to biological deterioration—such as certain detergents—be kept out of surface waters and ground waters. Enforcement and penalties should be strict.

* * * * *

14. Every owner and manager of land should be held responsible for permitting lethal pesticides or other materials to escape into water supplies, and should employ practices which prevent and control soil loss and resultant stream pollution by silt and other suspended materials.

Areas in pesticide control:

1. The League recognizes that control of pests is both desirable and necessary to the public interest.

2. The biological control of pests should be developed and applied to the fullest practicable extent. When pesticides are required for pest control, they should be of highly selective character.

3. Laws must be enacted at all governmental levels to fully protect the public from immediate and cumulative effects of pesticide use. These laws should recognize that the public interest goes beyond maintaining the public health to include protection of fish, wildlife, esthetic, and related values.

4. Among other laws, there should be a Federal law requiring close cooperation—beginning well in advance of any major proposed pesticide program—between all interested Federal agencies, and between Federal agencies and appropriate State agencies. This law should require that every request for major pesticide program authorization be accompanied by a fully comprehensive report of all agencies concerned—Federal, State, and local—such report to explain the nature and purpose of the proposed

program and the hazards which it would create, and to recommend formulations, dosages, and times and methods of application of the poisons. This law should further require that each of the affected agencies have personnel in the field during program implementation to insure full protection of the public interest.

5. Each State, at the least, should enact legislation to regulate custom applicators of pesticides. Such applicators should be required by law to be licensed by the State, and no license should be issued until the operator has demonstrated responsibility, and capability to properly handle and use pesticides. Severe penalties should be levied against applicators who employ practices which endanger the public interest, or who otherwise do not act in accordance with the State regulations. All law in this field, and enforcement of that law, must be based on standards which will insure maximum protection of the broad public interest.

6. Pesticide research must be public research to the extent necessary to protect the public interest, but should be private research with regard to development of products which are acceptable to the public. Pesticides manufacturers, rather than public agencies, should be required to prove clearly the "safety" of their products before they can be sold.

In concluding these excerpts, it should be pointed out that some will feel that these policies and principles are controversial. Some engineers, economists, and others are of the opinion that these are ideals and not realistic. However, in light of today's "Space Age," and I use this term with all it implies, nothing appears to be impossible. Surely, anything as important as our water deserves the best in planning, management, and use that can be obtained. It is incredible that we should settle for anything less. The foregoing statement might be likened in principle to the Ten Commandments. Both might be hard to live by, perhaps idealistic and unreal to some, but that does not make them wrong! If this issue has two sides, the Izaak Walton League and the greatest share of the populace prefer the side of the swinging pendulum that stands and works for the puritan viewpoint of clean waters in opposition to the camp that pollutes our waters to the greatest extent that they can get away with!

Some legislation that deals with agriculture and pollution was introduced in the first session of the Eighty-ninth Congress, with passage on several important fronts. On October 2, 1965, President Johnson signed the Water Quality Act of 1965 into Public Law 89-234. This short excerpt from the President's remarks sets the tone of this important measure:

The clear, fresh waters that were our national heritage have become dumping grounds for garbage and filth. They poison our fish, they breed disease, they despoil our landscapes.

No one has a right to use America's rivers and America's waterways that belong to all the people as a sewer. . . .

With the establishment of the new Iowa Water Pollution Control Commission, Iowa is in an extremely good position to work with this new federal legislation. Iowa is demonstrating its concern and interest in pollution abatement by the establishment of this new commission, holding meetings such as the one upon which this book is based, and by strong private organizational efforts. However, we will need continuing and even more effective efforts in water pollution abatement. When President Johnson signed the Water Quality Act he stated:

> The ultimate victory of reclaiming this portion of our national heritage really rests in the hands of all the people of America, not just the government here in Washington. Much of the money, some of the imagination, much of the effort, must be generated at local level. Then, and really only then, will this blueprint for victory become victory in fact.

Another new piece of federal legislation is the Water Resources Planning Act. Signed into law on July 22, 1965, it is important not only to agriculture but also to cities and industries. As its name implies, it should mean much to our future.

The passage by Congress of the Food and Agricultural Act of 1965 on October 12, 1965, made possible a more complete conservation and water pollution abatement program that will have effects on Iowa's agriculture. This act places more emphasis on conservation, and this would include water pollution abatement, than some previous programs in this area. This important change is one that should be expanded. While this country is in an era of overproduction that is resulting in surplus, research and production techniques should be developed that do not have detrimental side effects such as we are now experiencing in agriculture. One example along this line that is not the usual erosion or pesticide (chemical) problem would be the development of dairy wastes into a usable by-product; or, at least they should be handled in a more suitable manner so as not to become a stream pollutant.

The expansion and improvement of man's ability to live within his world without poisoning his environment or wasting his natural resources is squarely up to us.

CHAPTER 11

IOWA'S WATERS AND RECREATION

ARNOLD O. HAUGEN

WATERS HAVE BEEN AND WILL CONTINUE TO BE EXTREMELY IMPORTANT in the development of our country. The beaver, muskrat, and mink inhabiting the streams provided the incentive that lured the trapper-explorers and fur traders westward into the vast Indian country. These were the hardy, and often lawless, explorers who opened the routes for settlers into the frontier areas. The pristine streams provided highways for canoe and boat travel into unknown regions. Settlers harnessed the tumbling waters to provide power for gristmills and depended on the unspoiled streams and springs for water for livestock and household use.

Settlers arriving in Iowa found mainly a prairie landscape with streams bordered by ribbons of timber reaching like fingers out onto the open lands. Only in the northeast counties did they find as much as a quarter of the landscape covered by timber. It was here that my grandfather settled in the 1850's. Like other pioneers of his day he was looking for a place with water, woods, and plowland. Wetlands were especially abundant in the central and northern parts of Iowa, with 1,196,392 acres of such lands reported for 1850.[1] Pothole and marsh areas served as Iowa's "duck factories." The prairie chicken found nesting conditions to its liking on the unplowed, native grass covered, rolling hills between the wet areas. The prairie chicken and the buffalo were species belonging to the native prairie habitat.

ARNOLD O. HAUGEN is leader, Iowa Cooperative Wildlife Research Unit, Iowa State University, Ames, Iowa. The Unit is cooperatively sponsored by the Iowa State Conservation Commission; Iowa State University; U.S. Department of the Interior, Bureau of Sport Fisheries and Wildlife; and the Wildlife Management Institute.

167

Native wildlife was abundant enough in pioneer days to provide good sport for the sparse populations. Most hunters at the time, however, were more in need of meat than of sport. Establishing and improving a homestead did not leave time for leisure and sport hunting. In those days most people lived on the land, few in cities. Pollution was insignificant, and streams and lakes were generally regarded as safe for swimming. I can well remember many delightful days of swimming in the farm creek, back in World War I days. Then the only kind of swimming suit I knew was a birthday suit, and so far as I was concerned, the word "pollution" had not yet been coined.

IMPACTS OF MODERN-DAY LIVING

There is an old saying that time changes everything. How true that is, and how that has created problems for us. Iowa's urbanization trend has isolated a high percentage of our people from the land (69 per cent live in incorporated towns). Such crowding and the resultant sewage disposal problems and the effect of factories on water quality have created many problems for us. These are problems of our own making, because as William Cowper said, "God made the country, man made the town."

It is unfortunate that industrialization, which has lightened our burden of making a living and has given us more and more time for leisure, has also caused serious loss to our outdoor heritage—now so badly needed for outdoor recreation. Are we to be blessed with more time for leisure, yet doomed to enjoy it less?

Waters cover about 70 per cent of the earth's surface. Its total supply will not increase or decrease, but its quality has suffered and the extent of its use and reuse is increasing rapidly. Already, the Public Health Service estimates that the total flow of the Ohio River is being used 3.7 times before it reaches the Mississippi and that by the time the water in the Mahoning River reaches Youngstown, Ohio, it has been used 8 times.[2] Such waters under present conditions can hardly be regarded as safe for swimming or domestic consumption. The Public Health Service has isolated polio, infectious hepatitis, and more than thirty other live viruses which may carry disease, from sewage effluent.[3]

You will recall in the summer of 1965 we heard much publicity about the serious water shortage in the East. New York City was so short that restaurants would not serve a glass of water with meals unless the customer asked for it. Little publicity, however, was given to the fact that the mighty Hudson River, which pours millions of gallons a day past New York City, is so polluted that it cannot be used as an industrial water supply. Swimming in it is not safe below North

Tarrytown and fishing in it would provide little chance for success. New York City alone dumps 400 million gallons of raw sewage a day into the harbor. These examples may seem a long way from home. Let me remind you, however, that they are also examples of what can happen anywhere when cities are willing to sell their God-given birthrights for urban growth and settle for cheap ways to dispose of their wastes.

Dumping of raw sewage is only one of several ways by which pollution may seriously decrease or ruin the value of waters for recreation. The washing of pesticides, herbicides, wastes from manufacturing processes, and by-products from canneries and creameries into streams or lakes can produce equally disastrous pollution. The sinister effect of oil spills on water quality for recreation and on fish and waterfowl is well known. Such useful agricultural chemicals as fertilizers can also be damaging to recreational waters. Wherever too much fertilizer enters waters, an undesirable algal bloom may result. The raising of the temperature of a stream, as a result of the waters being used as a coolant in manufacturing, may make the stream unfit for certain kinds of desirable fish. Even the silting in of fish spawning areas and reservoirs and the roiling of waters as a result of erosion may be regarded as a type of pollution, a "creeping" type. In the disastrous flood that hit the Mississippi River in the spring of 1965, 800 billion gallons of water poured into the upper reaches of the river in a ten-day period. It has been estimated that the flood carried 340,000 tons of silt past St. Paul. The water raced down the channels when much of it should have been held back by millions of potholes, swamps, and marshes.

President Johnson, when signing the federal Water Pollution Control Act, summed up the problem when he stated:[4]

> The clear, fresh waters that were our national heritage have become dumping grounds for garbage and filth. They poison our fish, they breed disease, they despoil our landscape. . . . There is no excuse for a river flowing red with blood from slaughterhouses. There is no excuse for paper mills pouring tons of sulphuric acid into the lakes and the streams of the people of this country. There is no excuse—and we should call a spade a spade—for chemical companies and oil refineries using our major rivers as pipelines for toxic wastes. There is no excuse for communities to use other people's rivers as a dump for their raw sewage.

Perhaps pollution is like sin: It seems too tempting to ever be completely controlled. It will take a lot of preaching to minimize it. In "courting" new industry we should be as choosy as we were when we courted our best girl. We should put emphasis on inviting non-polluting types of industries to our state.

WATER RESOURCE FOR RECREATION

In Iowa 72 natural lakes provide roughly 43,700 surface-acres of water.[5] Twenty-five artificial small lakes provide another 4,733 acres. Slightly over 30,000 farm ponds have been built, and about 600 new ponds are being added each year. The Coralville reservoir provides 4,900 surface-acres of water at summer level. Additional acreage will be added with the completion of the Red Rock, Saylorville, and Rathbun reservoirs. Iowa is further blessed with the magnificent Mississippi and Missouri rivers on the east and west borders, respectively, and by the many beautiful smaller streams. About 100,000 of the roughly 1 million acres of wetlands which once dotted Iowa prairies remain.

This may sound as if Iowans are still blessed with a lot of water with much opportunity for water recreation. Water is the *number one feature* that nearly everyone looks for in outdoor recreation. However, to be valuable for recreation it must be *clean water* because, as stated by the Outdoor Recreation Resources Review Commission in its report to President Kennedy and Congress, "polluted water in the ocean, a lake, a river, or a reservoir is of little use for recreation."[6] This requirement automatically removes much of Iowa's water from use for some kinds of recreation. While water is not essential to all forms of recreation, it often adds immeasurably to the scene and to the quality of the outdoor experience.

One of our problems is that much of Iowa's water is not available to the recreation-minded public because the shorelines are privately owned and public access is lacking. Then, too, increasing quantities of our public waters are being polluted to the extent that (1) fish life is being killed or the species composition changed to less desirable forms, (2) swimming is no longer safe because of possible disease problems, and (3) the beauty of the scene has been seriously impaired. Channelization and straightening of streams has reduced the value of some waters for recreation. The drastic water level fluctuation which normally occurs on the large flood control reservoirs limits their value to recreation because of the bare, muddy, and uninviting shorelines exposed when the water level drops. The end result of all these factors is that both the quantity and the quality of waters for recreation in Iowa, as elsewhere, are limited and will need careful management if residents are to continue to enoy their heritage.

THE DEMAND FOR WATER RECREATION

Predictions on a national scale are that the human population will double and that the increase in leisure time will triple by the year 2000.[7] Louis Clapper has estimated that daily use and reuse of water will triple in the same period.[8] By 1980 we will probably be using 600 billion gallons of fresh water daily. Hydrologists have estimated that our maximum freshwater supply only amounts to 650 billion gallons per day. By the year 2000 we are expected to be using a trillion gallons per day. This saddles us with a tremendous responsibility for safeguarding our water quality. This spiraling of numbers and extra demand on water resources will create real competition for use of our water heritage. As an example, swimming in 1960 ranked second in popularity as an outdoor summer recreation, with 672 million occasions of participation. Predicted growth shows that by the year 2000 swimming will lead all other forms of outdoor recreation, with an expected 2.22 billion occasions of participation.[9]

We must recognize that man does not live by bread alone. Food and shelter alone will not make life worthwhile. With leisure time due to triple in the next thirty-five years, we are faced with the task of providing additional opportunities for people to enrich their lives through its better use. An adequate recreation program will help these crowded people live healthier and happier lives. Suitable outdoor recreation opportunities should help people of all ages and of either sex by improving them physically, mentally, and spiritually. Leisure is a fruit of life; we have the opportunity and responsibility to make wise use of it. Have we merely learned to earn a living, or to live a life worth living?

To provide satisfying outdoor recreation experiences for the people of Iowa, we will need suitably located interesting pieces of geography with clean water, forests, wildlife, and imaginative leadership for recreation resource management.

WATER MANAGEMENT RECOMMENDATIONS FOR RECREATION

In agreement with the Iowa Governor's Committee on Conservation of Outdoor Resources, the following recommendations are proposed for the management of Iowa's waters for recreation.

1. *Access sites to public waters.* It was urged that the state Conservation Commission and county conservation boards step up their programs to acquire and improve access sites to public waters for boating, fishing, and other appropriate uses. Special effort should be made to secure access sites where roads cross public waters suitable for recreation.

2. *Zoning for water recreation.* Development of a logical lake and stream classification is urged. This, however, does not imply that any of the waters of Iowa are to be classified as convenient "sewers" for permissive pollution.

To provide for orderly use of water for recreation, some type of zoning based on either area or time of use is recommended. Water skiing, scuba diving, fishing, and lake swimming are examples of activities that may conflict at times.

3. *Small watershed development.* It is urged that the Iowa State Conservation Commission, the Soil Conservation Service, farm groups, and other interested organizations cooperate in integrating significant wildlife and water development plans for recreation into small watershed development plans. Drainage of wetlands of value to waterfowl in watershed development areas is discouraged.

4. *Farm ponds.* Farmers who seek government assistance for constructing farm ponds should be urged to build the ponds as large as practicable. Fencing and cover plantings around such ponds will improve their wildlife and scenic value and recreational usefulness. The support of federal authorities for fencing and cover plantings of pond sites should be continued.

Opening privately constructed and managed fishing ponds to public use is also recommended.

5. *Roadside ponds.* It is recommended that road building authorities consider the possibility of constructing ponds at sites where dirt is borrowed for road grade fills. Cooperation among the Highway Commission, the county conservation boards, and the state Conservation Commission will enhance such a possibility.

6. *Wetlands.* Wetlands are of prime importance to many species of wildlife. It is recommended that a plan be developed for subsidy payments to landowners who are willing to leave wetland areas in a natural state, free from drainage. Financial support is recommended for flooding lowland to provide marshland for waterfowl and furbearers.

Further drainage of Iowa's rapidly dwindling supply of wetlands is discouraged. No payment of government subsidies should be made for drainage of ponds or wetlands, lands of marsh or pothole type.

7. *Wild rivers.* It is urged that Iowa designate extensive sections of at least one cold water stream, one prairie type stream and one loess area stream as wild rivers to remain free from major structures such as dams, channel straightening, and dikes. Rivers recommended for such designation include: for cold water streams, the Upper Iowa and parts of its tributaries, and possibly parts of the Yellow, Turkey, and Volga rivers; for prairie rivers, the Wapsipinicon and/or sections of the Des Moines; and for a loess area stream, the Little Sioux between Correctionville and Lake Okoboji. The purchase of "easements" or outright land purchase to provide protection against development that might cause further destruction of "wild values" is recommended.

8. *Shoreline zone.* The limited shoreline and other public wa-

ters in Iowa should be protected against further encroachment. State-wide regulations should be established to provide for a reasonable "set-back" (no building) shoreline zone.

9. *Public access.* One of the most important recommendations of the governor's committee is that the state Conservation Commission and county conservation boards expand their program to purchase shoreline areas or shoreline easements on lakes and streams. To facilitate such a program, it is recommended that a new law be passed to authorize the state Conservation Commission and county conservation boards to condemn for easements where such a procedure is necessary to procure shoreline and open space areas for public recreation. Even Iowa's first legislature was aware of the importance of public access to water. It is reported that those legislators voted on a bill to set aside a strip of public land along each of Iowa's meandered streams. Unfortunately, the proposed bill lost by one vote.

10. *Interstate park system.* An interstate compact to establish and coordinate operation of a park system along the scenic Mississippi River from Dubuque north into Minnesota is urged. A resolution calling for such a compact was passed in the recent session of the Iowa state legislature. The picturesque features of the land and a guarantee of clean waters in the Mississippi are essential to the development of such a recreation area.

These recommendations are far reaching in effect, and they should be. We are planning for the welfare and enjoyment of all of Iowa's 2.825 million citizens of today, and for the slightly over 4 million population predicted for the year 2000. Lands and waters for intensive outdoor recreation and the preservation of natural areas of water and lands for "wilderness" types must be planned for and acquired now. Tomorrow may be too late to protect our heritage against further misuse. On the basis of increasing costs, it is urgent that the program be started as soon as practicable. Since the recommended development is for the use of all citizens, it is appropriate that the program be financed mainly from legislative appropriations from the general fund.

An important question to ask ourselves regarding use of our natural resources is, "What have we done to promote their wise use?" We have not paid for our keep here on earth until we have contributed to preservation of our resource heritage for generations to come. If we have not contributed to a richer heritage for future generations, it will not matter how much money we have in the bank, we are poor—poor both morally and spiritually.

NOTES

1. Arnold O. Haugen, *Governor's Committee Report on Iowa's Outdoor Resources, Their Conservation and Use in Outdoor Recreation* (Des Moines, Iowa, 1963), p. 116.

2. Louis S. Clapper, "America's Shame, Water Pollution," *National Wildlife,* Vol. 1, No. 6 (1963), p. 10.
3. *Ibid.*
4. Wildlife Management Institute, "President Signs Water Polution Control Act," *Outdoor News Bulletin,* Vol. 19, No. 20 (1965), p. 1.
5. Glen G. Powers, *Report of the State Conservation Commission for the Biennium ending June* 30, 1962 (Des Moines, Iowa, Iowa State Conservation Commission, 1963), pp. 50–51.
6. Outdoor Recreation Resources Review Commission, *Outdoor Recreation for America* (Washington, D.C., 1962), p. 70.
7. *Ibid.,* p. 32.
8. Clapper (1963).
9. Outdoor Recr. Res. Rev. Comm. (1962), p. 46.

DISCUSSION

WILLIAM M. MILLER

THE IMPORTANCE OF WATER RESOURCES IN HELPING TO SATISFY THE REC-reational needs of the people of Iowa has been ably discussed by Dr. Arnold Haugen. One has only to observe the large increase in the number of boats, even in inland areas, to realize that the popularity of water sports is at an all-time high. Further, as leisure time and population density increase, improved and expanded usable water resources will be required.

There is no question but that pollution of public waters will render them undesirable for recreational use and inhospitable to wildlife. In fact, it is possible for pollution to be so bad as to make waters completely useless for any activity except transportation. This has already happened in many waterways in this nation and abroad. Fortunately, Iowa streams have generally not been degraded to this extent and are still extensively used by its citizens and industry. We want to keep it that way.

RESPONSIBILITY FOR CONTROL

The chemical industry, through the Manufacturing Chemists Association, pledges itself to cooperate fully with efforts to control pollution. Its policy, as stated in the following principles, was published a number of years ago.

> The surface waters are one of the nation's valuable, renewable natural resources. This vital resource must not be destroyed by uncontrolled stream

WILLIAM M. MILLER is plant manager, Ortho Division, Chevron Chemical Company, Fort Madison Plant, Fort Madison, Iowa.

pollution. The chemical industry, as well as all other industry, has a great stake in this water resource. Growth and development depend upon it.

Proper control of stream pollution is one of the obligations of responsible corporate citizenship.

The chemical industry recognizes the community nature of water pollution control and desires to cooperate fully with the control agencies that are responsible for safeguarding the health and welfare of the people.

When new laws and ordinances are being considered, the chemical industry pledges itself to be a constructive contributor in promoting measures which will be sound, effective and equitable.

Long before this statement was published in 1961, the chemical industry had an extensive program of pollution control under way. Similar programs can be adopted by city, state, agriculture, and the public sector.

It must be recognized that we are not only users but reusers of our natural water resources. The water in our streams must be used many times before it returns to the sea. Water pollution can be caused by nearly every human activity from space and atomic programs to hand washing. If every user contributes to the pollution problem, the job of water cleanup is soon so difficult and costly that no one agency or industry can hope to accomplish the task. The spiral begins—the polluted streams drive wildlife, sportsmen, industry, and prosperity away. The problem cannot be reduced to a satisfactory level unless all segments of society and the economy which share responsibility for water use and misuse take corrective action.

At the same time it should be recognized that the problems of water pollution vary greatly in their type, causes, severity, and effects on society from region to region. Solutions to the problems are most often unique to the environmental situation involved. One rule or one set of standards is most likely not applicable to all cases. There is effluent from farm, home, city, and industry; each source has its contributor, each demanding a different solution, and it is imperative that contributions from each source be controlled to a realistic minimum. Each problem must be identified and its unique solution sought.

SETTING WATER STANDARDS

This brings us to our next task and perhaps the most difficult. We must establish realistic standards which will maintain our waterways in a state satisfactory for all reusers. These standards must be equitable and must take into consideration reusers of water whose primary concern is not necessarily recreational or conservation. The three bodies, agricultural, industrial, and political, must be responsible for their contribution to the general problem. It must be recognized that these three bodies are interdependent. Any standard should recognize this interdependence and while each problem may need its own solution, each solution and the standards which establish the level of performance should be compatible with the ultimate interdependence of all segments of the society.

After the problem has been identified and standards set, we face our next problem and that is one of education. The seminar upon which this book is based is an excellent example of the type of education required. The chemical industry is doing the same internally.

EDUCATION

A series of industry workshop programs which have to do specifically with the control of pollution, both in water and air, have been held throughout the country. Teams of chemical experts and technicians have met to consider the problem. For example, there was a meeting in Austin, Texas, on September 13, 1965; another in Denver, October 28, 1965; and one in Michigan, November 15, 1965, in addition to meetings in Los Angeles, San Francisco, and Portland, Oregon.

Several technical and informative brochures have been prepared by the chemical industry which outline such responsibilities as the proper gathering of individual plant data, management responsibility, etc. The training programs now go beyond the industry itself to include its customers and end users who, through careful control of the chemical products used as directed by the supplier, can aid the pollution control problem. But other programs are necessary in the public sector. How does improper land management contribute to pollution problems? Why must municipalities build sewage disposal plants? These questions asked by the public must be answered, and financial justification for the necessary expenditures explained.

FINANCIAL RESPONSIBILITY

Another aspect of the problem is financial responsibility. Continued clean water or improved water quality is not possible without the expenditure of funds. We in industry have spent millions to clean up plant effluent and will continue to do so. We hold very fundamentally to our community responsibility as a corporate citizen to support clean water efforts and improved recreational uses. Not only must monies continue to be spent in capital construction in all sectors of the community but we must also spend monies for research and development and education. This will cost money—lots of it. Without public recognition of the financial facts of this endeavor, an adequate program cannot be implemented.

There are no basic differences among responsible citizens in the belief that pollution must be controlled and abated. Any differences that may exist revolve around how to accomplish control and abatement without adversely affecting the economy of Iowa.

DISCUSSION

J. MERRILL ANDERSON

EVERYONE AGREES THAT THE DEMAND FOR WATER FOR RECREATION AND wildlife will grow tremendously. Intensive use of beaches, lakeshores, and parks and forest areas that contain streams and ponds shows the growing demand for recreation facilities. In 1955, 50 million people visited national parks and monuments—two and a half times the number of visitors in 1940. By 1960 these visitors had increased to 79 million. More than 46 million went to national forests for recreation in 1955, and 92.5 million in 1960. In 1960, 25 million people fished and 15 million hunted.

As the population grows and leisure time increases, the demand for recreational use grows. Everyone is "for" recreation—like progress and the hope of Heaven. Dr. Arnold Haugen stated that the Outdoor Recreation Resources Review Commission predicts that by the year 2000 America's population is expected to double and its recreational demand to triple.

The American Farm Bureau Federation's 1965 policies included this paragraph:

> It is the obligation of each generation to make wise use of our natural resources, with particular regard to the needs of future generations. This can best be accomplished by emphasis on participation and responsibility of individuals, private organizations, and local and state units of government in the investigation, planning, and administration of the development and use of natural resources.

Water and the problems and issues related to it are vital subjects. Farmers have a very direct interest because management of water involves an important resource of rural areas. Our goal should be the wise, cooperative, and multiple use of our land and water to the greatest future benefit of all people. It will be a big job to make certain that people, not only in Iowa but in the large metropolitan centers as well, have a place to live and breathe. The demands upon our recreational facilities are probably increasing faster than we recognize them and faster than the capabilities of our current programs.

There has been a flurry of new legislation pertaining to the use of public and privately owned watershed facilities and an impressive number of bills have been passed. In 1965 our legislature adopted a comprehensive Water Pollution Control Act, creating an independent state commission representing various interests (including the farmer,

J. MERRILL ANDERSON is president, Iowa Farm Bureau Federation.

for which we are thankful) to make policy, develop programs, and direct enforcement of pollution control measures.

Congress in 1965 sent to the President a Water Pollution Control Act authorizing the establishment in the Department of Health, Education, and Welfare of a federal Water Pollution Control Administration, and the appointment of an additional assistant secretary to supervise it, all under the general authority of the Secretary of HEW. This measure includes $20 million for federal matching grants to seek improved methods for preventing untreated sewage and wastes from being discharged into bays and rivers from storm water sewers or from combined storm and sanitary sewers. The measure also increased grants by $50 million for construction of community sewage treatment plants and outlined a system for states to (1) establish water quality standards for interstate waters or portions thereof within the state and (2) to enforce these standards, and if the state fails to do these HEW can propose standards.

Another bill authorized $55 million a year for a program of matching grants to develop water supply and waste disposal systems in rural areas. This bill authorized $50 million annually in matching grants to soil and water associations and local public agencies for construction of water supply and sewage disposal systems in rural areas where the population does not exceed 5,500. (The 1965 Housing Act already makes grants to larger communities.) Five million dollars is to be used to prepare comprehensive plans for development of water supply or sewage disposal systems. Farmers Home Administration authorized loans and loan insurance for waste disposal systems were also increased.

The farm bill allows government to pay farmers for special conservation practices to convert farmland into hunting preserves. It turns money, too, over to cities and states to buy farmland for recreation purposes, though not much of this land is expected to be found to have the natural appeal that is needed for parks. Under Title IV—Cropland Adjustment—the secretary is authorized to enter into five- to ten-year contracts with farmers, calling for conversion of cropland into vegetable cover, water storage facilities, or other soil, water, wildlife, or forest conserving uses.

Available from the federal level is funding from the Farmers Home Administration for loans to develop agricultural lands and facilities into recreational use as additional sources of farm income. Loans are also available to associations for development of recreational potential in rural areas. Land and water conservation funds for 1966 totaled about $125 million, of which $75 million went to states on a matching basis to develop and acquire land for expansion of state recreational facilities. Large additional sums are available for direct federal expenditures since nearly all federal projects include recreational development.

In July, 1965, an act was passed creating a Water Resources Council, authorizing the establishment of federal-state river basin commissions with broad planning authority. Such commissions may have a dominant role to play in the development of basin resources.

An amendment to the Watershed Protection and Flood Prevention Act authorized both financial and technical assistance to local groups in developing watershed recreation. The USDA can help the populace of watershed areas enlarge dams to form larger bodies of water; build new reservoirs specifically for recreation use; improve natural lakes, streams, or shorelines; and pay costs of recreational facilities bordering water. The amendments were intended to help meet increasing public demand for water-based outdoor recreation facilities.

Among the federal agencies involved with recreation are five different bureaus in the Department of the Interior, two in the Department of Commerce, six in the USDA, two in HEW, and the Corps of Engineers in the Department of Defense.

The multiplicity of government agencies in the field of water resources development has reached serious proportions. The second Hoover Commission listed ten such agencies in the Department of the Interior alone, and this is only one of four Cabinet-rank federal departments having responsibility in the field. No less than five new bureaus or agencies have been added since the Hoover Commission report, and the Eighty-ninth Congress undoubtedly added more. In summary, federal and state activity is being expanded through every agency of government that deals with land, water, highways, and public health, in addition to many others. All plans for watershed management, public works, community and rural development, industrial development, highway planning, public health, public land management, and fish and wildlife programs include provisions for recreation.

In 1965 several major state and national water measures were enacted and the American people began to be more conscious of the importance of water in their lives.

A second important trend is the increase in construction of farm ponds. These ponds dot the landscape. Dr. Haugen stated that to 1965 over 30,000 had been built in Iowa, and about 600 are being added each year. Farmers are adding substantially to the water recreational facilities of our state through these ponds. They are an excellent example of facilities that are privately owned but generally used by the public. The farm pond on my land has resulted in many interesting experiences. Town folks are frequent visitors. Some respect private property, others do not. It appears that about all you have to do today is create a puddle and people start driving up to swim, fish, boat, hunt, picnic, or just look.

Water for recreation needs to be clean and in pleasant surroundings. If such water is available, the recreational benefits to the public will be substantial. Water is the key element in many kinds of recreation. It is indispensable to wildlife, which is valuable to recreation. It needs to be stable enough to avoid exposing mud flats or leaving boat docks stranded during the season of use. Will this be a problem with the Saylorville and Red Rock dams?

Water is neither withdrawn nor consumed for recreation and wildlife uses, although some is lost to evaporation and seepage. But withdrawal and consumptive uses, such as irrigation and industry, often reduce the supply or diminish the value of water for recreation and wildlife. Thus, the supply and use of water for recreation and wildlife cannot be measured in gallons, as it is for withdrawal uses. Rather, availability and character of lakes, streams, and other bodies of water to meet the needs in each location are crucial matters.

Farmers and ranchers should recognize that drainage from feedlots, farmsteads, and fields is clearly pollution if such drainage contributes material objectionable to others in their use of water for private, public, industrial, community, or recreational purposes. The continued increase in the use of herbicides and insecticides is also a potential danger to water supplies, but these are necessary for the production of high-quality food at relatively low cost to consumers. Farmers need to cooperate on an educational program for the proper use of agricultural chemicals and drugs. They favor continued research on water pollution within the framework of federal-state-private cooperation.

Resource planning and use is moving rapidly into the context of public policy and public action. Traditionally, America has considered the quantity of these resources and used them freely in the building of our country. The obvious needs of the present and the future require that we look upon the qualitative as well as quantitative use of our resources and assume an increasing responsibility to assure that the resources will be used in a manner that will guarantee maximum utility in serving both private and public interests.

Farmers, along with industry, road builders, and others, admit they are responsible for draining many acres of marshes, sloughs, and ponds that would be valuable to waterfowl. Some landowners, however, are deliberately increasing marsh areas to produce wildlife. We can anticipate many future problems in the demand for more recreational use of water. If priority in the use of water must be established, human consumption and use for food production would rank higher than recreational use.

Landowners are concerned today with the problem caused by the encroachment on private property by the demands of the public. Right of access, easements, and condemnations are viewed with alarm by many farmers who have paid dearly and worked hard to own property. County conservation boards should develop natural resources, but within reason. Farmers are urged to cooperate with county conservation boards to assure responsible use of tax funds in establishing and maintaining worthwhile programs. Farm liability is another problem. Should a pond be considered a necessary part of the property on which it is located or is it considered an "attractive nuisance?" It is readily apparent that there are many complexities to this question.

It should be noted further that the trend of authority to set standards of quality is shifting from state to federal level. The Water Pollution Control Act passed by Congress in 1965 is an example. Some may not feel this is a danger, but we believe most decisions should be made at the local and state level. The right to the use of water and the authority under which such rights are allocated are rapidly becoming more acute issues. In recent years Supreme Court decisions have tended to remove authority from the states in this field and place it in the hands of the federal government. The *California* vs. *Arizona* case, decided June 3, 1963, is an example. Here the Court granted a federal officer sole power to allocate the surplus water of the Colorado River without regard to state law.

The pressure for federal legislation and funding is accelerating and poses major questions relative to federal control of such resources. We recognize there are conflicting demands on water resources for many purposes, and this necessitates a coordinated approach to resolve such conflicts. State and local planning committees can do this job best.

Many leaders are predicting farmers will soon be asked to go into full production because of world food shortages, especially those in Asia and South America. If this becomes necessary, competition for recreational areas and water will become more intense. Great volumes of water would be used if new lands were developed by irrigation.

CHAPTER 12

THE WONDERFUL WORLD OF WATER

ROBERT L. SMITH

INASMUCH AS THE FOREGOING CHAPTERS ARE DEVOTED TO SPECIFIC ASPECTS of water quality control, it would appear appropriate to broaden our interest and consider the general ingredients of water management problems. The "Wonderful World of Water" represents a truly fascinating, though often perplexing, area of endeavor. Brief exploration of this observation may provide some added insight to the nature and significance of the technical and policy action decisions which are the subject of this book.

One commodity easily obtainable in the field of water management is free advice. The public administrator in water—local, state, or federal—soon learns this lesson in the day-to-day correspondence he receives from a concerned constituency. Often such communications provide some useful insight, personal or public, not otherwise available to the administrator. At times they provide humorous anecdotes not found in conventional storybooks. For example, an administrator with a federal resources agency once received an urgent dispatch requesting that he implement a program for planting trees along a river so that boards could be nailed to them when they grew to sufficient stature, thus forming a protective levee. Or one might cite an earnest multipage letter, received by the Iowa Natural Resources Council, which advocated construction of a major equalizer canal along the Iowa-Minnesota border. The purpose of the canal was supposedly to provide flood relief by diverting floods to and from the

ROBERT L. SMITH is Glen L. Parker Professor of Water Resources, University of Kansas, Lawrence, Kansas.

Missouri and Mississippi rivers. The letter acknowledged that right-of-way might be costly but assured one and all that the costs thereof could be easily discharged by the mineral wealth, including "reinforced concrete," that would be unearthed. The letter gave little attention to such matters as the effective hydraulic performance of such a facility.

One point should be clearly understood. Letters such as those cited are not written facetiously but with utmost sincerity. They represent the views of a concerned public, and often they are prompted by prior personal tragedy. The American public has become most conscious of water management problems. Admittedly, this consciousness is often bred and nourished by vested interest considerations but on the whole results from two special characteristics of water which are: (1) its migratory nature and (2) its capacity to fulfill and satisfy an extraordinarily diverse pattern of wants, each of which is related to the social desires and economic needs of one or more individuals, private corporations, and political units.

In tandem these two factors present a major dilemma. The migratory feature makes it most difficult to satisfy one portion of the demand characteristic without affecting, to greater or lesser degree and oftentimes adversely, another portion of the demand function. Thus, what constitutes good water management is not easily defined. And nowhere is the management problem more complex than in the area of water quality. The trouble is that good water resources management requires resolution of the relevant importance, to any given situation, of the pertinent aspects of existing health, transportation, power, conservation, land management, and agricultural policies, etc. As important as each of these matters is to our society, or to specific groups of water users, *we cannot permit any one area to control all water management decisions if we are to achieve maximum practical utilization of the resource, and if we are to serve the variable water needs of the people.*

Now there may be some who will quarrel with the contention that recognition of these two characteristics—migratory nature and diverse utility—is fundamental to understanding of our water management problems. But the first is adequately documented in the laws of nature, and the second is continually observed in contemporary America. Each individual assigns a different relative value scale to the various water uses, but everyone desires it for one or more purposes. The significance of this situation can be simply stated. The world of water is inherently full of conflict—conflict between man and nature, conflict between political jurisdictions, conflict between users, and conflict between social value judgments which of themselves are biased by personal needs and wants.[1]

How to analyze both the physical and social ingredients of the problem and to postulate effective solutions comprises much of the fascination of the world of water. In this respect the situation does indeed cover the intellectual waterfront. From engineer to behavioral scientist there are problems to contemplate. In earlier days the theologian was often consulted, and it should be noted that the present state of water knowledge in many of the disciplines is such that his services are not inappropriate today. Why is it so?—because in the first instance man is in conflict with nature when he tries to alter the distribution of water to meet his needs. As such, he is dealing with forces which, in the extreme, he has not been able to measure. In short he cannot reproduce the entire device and test it in the laboratory. In addition he often fails to resolve his conflicts with his fellow man owing to his inability to quantify or measure the value of water for various uses on a universally acceptable scale. And finally, he is not dealing with a static problem. The physical characteristics of the resource and the social wants and needs and the values attached thereto are forever changing and yesterday's solution can be tomorrow's folly.

The inherent conflict cited earlier also leads to an observation that the world of water generates much political action. In a democratic society such inherent conflict of views demands some sort of social action. The record speaks for itself. Our legislative bodies have outdone themselves in seeking a solution to the "water problem." In the years since the first seminar on Iowa's water resources was held, we have seen the inception of such major federal efforts as the following:

1. The Water Pollution Control Act of 1956.
2. Implementation of the program of saline water conversion.
3. The Water Supply Act of 1958.
4. The appointment of a Select Senate Committee on Natural Water Resources.
5. The Water Pollution Control Act of 1961.
6. The Water Resources Research Act of 1964.
7. The Land and Water Conservation Fund Act of 1964.
8. The Water Quality Act of 1965.
9. The Water Resources Planning Act of 1965.
10. The Federal Water Project Recreation Act of 1965.

The foregoing list is not complete, nor does it give any hint of the added impact of such associated efforts as are represented by the Public Works and Economic Development Act, Housing and Urban Development Act, annual public works appropriation bills, the Consolidated Farmers Home Administration Act, or the many related state and local efforts.

Obviously, the world of water is a world of political action. But with such a maze of policy action, and the attendant treatment such action is accorded by the press, it is also a confusing world. Consider, for example, the young housewife of average intelligence who, through club activity, becomes interested in the water problem and the need for pollution control. After intensive reading in various magazines and journals she becomes vitally interested in the local scene. Accordingly she writes the mayor as follows:

Dear Sir:
    Yesterday's paper carried a brief note that the city is about to adopt plans for a new sewage treatment plant and is also authorizing a feasibility study of a new water supply impoundment on Pumpkin Creek. I am preparing a report on the city's water problems for our club meeting. My investigations to date indicate the federal government has a limited program of assistance for pollution abatement, but much more is needed. Could you tell me how much federal financial assistance, if any, is contemplated in the construction of the treatment plant? Also, why are you considering another dam on Pumpkin Creek? The articles I've read would indicate we should give consideration to using our heavily mineralized groundwater by building a saline conversion plant.

Subsequently she receives a letter which reads:

Dear Madam:
    In response to your recent inquiry I must advise as follows. We do plan to seek federal funds for the treatment plant. The exact amount is not yet determined. You should know that my top administrative aid and our consultants have been studying this matter intensively. There are several routes we might utilize and we want to be sure we find the solution which provides optimum opportunity to the city. We do not contemplate the use of a conversion plant. The Superintendent of Municipal Utilities advises that of the 40 cents you now pay per 1000 gallons of water only 5 to 10 cents can be charged to treatment costs. This is appreciably less than the latest available figures on conversion costs which do not include allowances for disposal of the collected brine. Moreover, we are not anxious to accept any additional disposal problems at this time.

One cannot help but wonder if in the recent legislative history in the world of water there is not an analogy with "bull market" action on Wall Street. Although this analogy is seldom appraised, decision to invest in a government program is not unlike a decision to invest in a stock. The primary difference is that we seldom reappraise the portfolio, we just add thereto. It seems safe to assume that our decisions to invest in governmental programs, like the stock market, are based on several approaches: analysis of fundamentals; use of charts, trends, and projections; and possibly fashion or vogue. A case could be made that all three approaches have been utilized in developing our present policies.

And thus we come to a question. How do we maintain perspective in the "Wonderful World of Water"? I am not sure this question can be easily answered. The emotional and vested interest ingredients make true perspective most difficult. However, the answer must be found in the political process. In our society establishment of perspective and resolution of the many local and subregional conflicts, which in the aggregate represent the nation's water problem, demand appreciable public understanding of alternative choices. We have a mechanism for undertaking this choice which we call the democratic process. This process is actually a very sophisticated computer which specializes in systems analysis. But like its mechanical counterparts it is most responsive to the data input. The time-honored equation of all computer systems, $GI = GO$, or garbage in equals garbage out, is equally applicable here. Adequate programming for this system, if we are to avoid future mismanagement, is going to require (1) an improved body of knowledge and (2) a concerted effort to translate this knowledge into factual and understandable courses of public policy. Several of the recently enacted policies appear to provide either opportunity or need to honor one or both of these points. How they are implemented may affect appreciably our future perspective.

The Water Resources Research Act was long overdue. There can be no quarrel with the stated objectives of this legislation. In every discipline we need to increase our knowledge concerning water. Beginning with the role of water in nature and continuing through an understanding of how it affects the behavioral action of man, we need to know appreciably more in order to grasp or even approximate the physical, economic, and social significance of various water management policies. Whether or not this act will represent a good investment, however, will be most dependent on whether the products of the research effort are translated into identifiable and understandable alternative choices of political and social policy.

There are those in the field of engineering and physical science who may feel that these comments leave room only for research in the social sciences, or that only applied research is being advocated. Not at all. We are simply stressing the point that research alone is not enough. Management perspective is gained only when the significance of the new knowledge, not just the discovery, is adequately explained. In the world of water, with its inherent social conflicts, this means translation to easily understandable policy terms for resources management is and will continue to remain a direct function of political action.

Our most concerted legislative actions in the past decade have been directed toward problems of water quality control. The Water Quality Act of 1965 presents a situation where our aforementioned requirement of "concerted effort to translate knowledge into factual and understandable courses of public policy" faces a real challenge. The act increases appreciably the federal government's regulatory authority in matters of water quality and provides for the adoption of standards of water quality. These provisions for establishing standards are intended to allow recognition of socially desirable broader values, as well as public health considerations, in the future quality management of our waters.

There was much controversy associated with passage of this bill. Not surprisingly, a great deal of the argument arose over who would set the standards—state or federal government. The real issue, when considered in water management perspective, is not who sets the standards but what is to be the basis of their determination. It is inconceivable that the concept of an attempt toward establishment of standards not responsible to the climatic, physiographic, and cultural factors associated with a given water source will prove satisfactory to anyone. However, there has been much reference to uniform standards in both professional and lay circles. Uniformity does have the appeal of consistency, but there is no advantage in being consistent if one is consistently wrong. Uniform criteria, if established at a level physically obtainable throughout a basin or a state (let alone a nation), would be too low to be significant. In fact they would prove damaging to water quality management. Uniform criteria set too high can impose an economic burden not commensurate with need and actually can create an unrealistic concept of water preservation rather than water conservation. The two terms are not synonymous. One implies retirement, the other indicates management and use. These stakes are high indeed. This program will require a concerted effort to translate knowledge into factual and understandable courses of alternative action.

A third program, in which there appears to be opportunity for contributing added perspective in the world of water, involves the Water Resources Planning Act of 1965. This act provides for the establishment of a federal Water Resources Council and the possible creation of river basin commissions. The federal council is charged with coordination of federal water resources programs and is to administer a program of federal grants to states for water resources planning.

Coordination has long been an overworked and often abused word. But if we are to maintain any reasonable perspective, someone must exercise forceful and meaningful coordination procedures. In water more than any other area the balanced viewpoint that results from adequate coordination is needed. Those two characteristics of water we noted earlier—migratory nature and diversified utility— demand that our efforts be coordinated. Formal assignment of this responsibility to a specific office, as in the case of the Water Resources Research Act, was long overdue. Effective implementation of this responsibility is going to require the exercise of authority in areas heretofore deemed the vested right of individual agencies and organizations. For example, the authorities established in this act will have to be reconciled with those contained in the Water Quality Act of 1965.

Similarly, the need for more adequate state and regional planning, when viewed the nation over, has been most apparent. The majority of our water problems are local or subregional in character, and it follows that various regions and states have different economic and social wants when it comes to the management of water. The desirability of identifying these needs by individual political unit is becoming well recognized. However, the necessity of analyzing the economic and social consequences to each political unit which would result from alternative courses of action is often overlooked in the development of both basic program policies and individual project plans.

For example, extension of low-cost water transport to a given area may not bring needed industrial growth even if project benefits (as measured by transportation savings) exceed project costs. Under certain conditions it may lead to exportation of the region's new products for processing elsewhere while preempting the use of water for other purposes.[2] Similarly, refusal to allow any degradation of selected waters in a region having an established recreational economy may seriously limit needed future diversification of the region's economic base. One can only conclude that if the Water Resources Planning Act will lead to a clear definition of our water needs, and the consequences associated with alternative means of fulfilling these needs are understood, the opportunity for a concerned public to gain needed perspective will be enhanced.

We have stated that the "Wonderful World of Water" is fascinating. It is fascinating for the human problems ranging from humor to tragedy that it encounters, for the conflicts it displays, for the scientific and intellectual challenge it poses, and for the political action it generates. And we have suggested that the most fascinating aspect of all is the constant search for perspective in an ever changing environment. Some may not agree with this view of water. They may feel it is too "polluted" with controversy, confusion, and politics. They may wish to point out that, above all else, the "Wonderful World of Water" has been a world of accomplishment from Babylonia to the Tennessee Valley, and we would agree. And they might contend that this discussion should practice what it preaches and provide an example of alternative courses of action. To fulfill this latter need we would repeat a quotation which contains both alternative and perspective.[3]

> Oh, the glamour and the clamor
> That attend affairs of state
> Seem to fascinate the rabble
> And impress some folks as great.
> But the truth about the matter
> In the scale of loss or gain—
> Not one inauguration's worth
> A good, slow, two-inch rain.

NOTES

1. For a more detailed discussion see R. L. Smith, "Institutional Programs to Meet Water Resources Needs," *Proceedings, 8th Annual Water for Texas Conference* (Texas A & M University, 1963).
2. *Ibid.*
3. A. P. Duggan, "Texas Ground Water Law," *Proceedings, Texas Water Law Conference*, 1952, cites Texas State Senator Carlos Ashley as the author of this jingle.

INDEX